BRITISH
FIRE BRIGADES

Part 2

**WILTSHIRE, GLOUCESTERSHIRE,
SOMERSET & AVON
(including the Fire Service College)**

Former City of Gloucester PE (Ford D600/Pyrene FFH 960K) has been preserved by Forest Studio Publications, Burley, Hampshire. It was collected from Gloucester by Fire Brigade Society Southern Area Secretary Simon Adamson (centre) who is pictured outside 05 with ADO Alan Murgatroyd and Fm Brian Kemmett. It has a 50' Merryweather escape.

ABBREVIATIONS — APPLIANCES

AccU	Accident unit	P	Pump (with 30' or 35' extension ladder)
Amb	Ambulance		
BAT	Breathing apparatus tender	PHP	Pump hydraulic platform
BL	Breakdown lorry	PL	Pump (with 45' extension ladder)
CaV	Canteen van		
CIU	Chemical incident unit	PE	Pump escape
CrT	Crash tender	ResT	Rescue tender
CRU	Cliff rescue unit	RIV	Rapid intervention vehicle
CU	Control unit	RT	Rescue tender
DCU	Damage control unit	RV	Rescue vehicle
DU	Decontamination unit	ST	Salvage tender
ERA	Emergency rescue appliance	TL	Turntable ladder
ET	Emergency tender	TLP	Turntable ladder pump
FbT	Fire boat	Tr	Trailer
FoT	Foam tender	TV	Towing vehicle
FST	Foam salvage tender	WrA	Water appliance
FTP	Foam tender pump	WrC	Water carrier
GPL	General purpose lorry	WrL	Water tender (with 45' extension ladder)
GPV	General purpose vehicle		
HFoT	Hose layer/foam tender	WrL/R	Water tender (with 45' extension ladder & full rescue equipment)
HL	Hose layer		
HP	Hydraulic platform		
HRT	Hose reel tender	WrT	Water tender (with 30' or 35' extension ladder)
L2P	Light two wheel drive vehicle with pump		
L4P	Light four wheel drive vehicle with pump	WrT/E	Water tender (with 35' extension and escape ladder)
L4T	Light four wheel drive vehicle with hosereel	WrT/L	Water tender (with 45' & 35' extension ladders)
L4V	Light four wheel drive vehicle	(DS)	Divisional spare
		(DI)	Driving instruction
LU	Lighting unit	(RS)	Reserve appliance
MRT	Major rescue tender	(WS)	Workshops vehicle

ABBREVIATIONS — FIRE STATIONS

D/M	Day manning	R/T	Retained
N/M	Nucleus manning	W/T	Wholetime

Top cover picture shows Avon B6 WrT HAE 880X (Dodge/HCB-Angus) with wheels painted in red & white quarters. This experiment, under evaluation, followed a suggestion by B6 Fm. Gordon Feaver; such markings, used in Sweden & Denmark give the moving WrT a stroboscopic effect. Bottom picture shows thatched house fire at Roxhill House, Lake, Amesbury, Wiltshire (25/3/83) with 3/5 WrL/R OHR 623R (now at 3/3).

INTRODUCTION

After a considerable delay I am pleased to present part 2 of British Fire Brigades. The booklets are designed to give information about the brigades and the individual fire stations with illustrations of the relative appliances.

I am indebted to the Chief Fire Officers and personnel of the brigades included and the Commandant and staff of the Fire Service College, for without their assistance it would not have been possible to produce this booklet.

It should be remembered that a booklet of this type goes out of date even before it is printed and so some of the fire stations have had a change of appliance since the photograph was taken. However we have done our best to update the information to take into consideration forthcoming changes.

It is intended that the information will be updated when reprints are required.

In the preparation of this booklet considerable assistance has been received from the FIRE BRIGADE SOCIETY which aims to link together all persons, regardless of nationality or creed, who have an interest in the fire fighting service, fire appliances and installations, or the prevention and extinction of fire. A special acknowledgement is given to Simon Adamson.

With the authorisation of the respective Chief Fire Officers, the next booklet in this series will cover the brigades of Mid Glamorgan, South Glamorgan, West Glamorgan and Gwent.

S.N.R.

BRITISH FIRE BRIGADES SERIES

Part 1 of British Fire Brigades, which dealt with the Brigades of Hampshire, Dorset and the Isle of Wight is still available. Copies can be obtained from your local Fire Services National Benevolent Fund secretary or direct from Forest Studio Publications, Forest Studio, Burley, Ringwood, Hants BH24 4AB (tel. 04253 2430) price £1.50 incl. p & p. It is the intention to cover every fire brigade in the UK in the series of about 20 booklets.

FIRE ENGINE RALLY

Preserved appliances from all over the country attend the annual Fire Engine Rally held every July at Crown Meadows, Blandford, Dorset. Proceeds are in aid of the Fire Services National Benevolent Fund.

Pictured here are three views from the 1982 rally; top to bottom; Ex. Somerset FB (02) 1953 Dennis F12 PE PYA 272 (left) pres. by N. Troake, Wellington with ex. Fort Dunlop Rubber Co., (Birmingham) 1955 Bedford SB WrT TCA 584 pres. by B.V. Lane, Cullompton; ex. Avon Rubber (Melksham) Works FB 1926 Dennis pump WV 6060, pres. by T. Richards, Bridport and being filmed by TVS cameraman Dave Davies; ex. Paignton FB (Devon) 1938 Leyland PE (50' Ajax escape) CDV 592 pres. by J. Weller, Exeter with ex. Bristol then Salisbury 1938 Leyland/Merryweather 100' GHW 415, pres. by Maidenhead personnel.

WILTSHIRE FIRE BRIGADE

The Wiltshire Fire Brigade was formed on de-nationalisation on April 1st 1948 and it comprised of 24 stations. A retained station at Market Lavington (south of Devizes) was shut down almost immediately and a voluntary station at Aldbourne (near Ramsbury) was closed in the mid 1960s.

A new D/M station at Stratton St. Margaret on the eastern side of Swindon was opened in 1975 and now there are a total of 23 stations (2 W/T, 2 D/M, 2 N/M & 17 R/T). Long term plans include completely new stations at Toothill (west side of Swindon) and Downton (south of Salisbury).

The Brigade Headquarters has been situated in a large country house at Potterne (south of Devizes) since late 1948. The Brigade is split into North (13 stations) and South (10 stations) Divisions with Div. HQs at Swindon and Salisbury. The Brigade was not affected by the 1974 boundary changes.

The new control room at HQ has just been completed and on average will handle about 5,000 calls a year with computer aided mobilising and rapid print teleprinters along with pocket alerters.

All the present stations have been built since 1953, the majority in the last 20 years.

Swindon and Salisbury are the major towns with areas of 'B' risk. The larger towns rate 'C' risk while the majority of the county is rural and therefore 'D' risk.

The county has a large number of military establishments, many situated around the vast area of Salisbury Plain. Manufacturing industries include rubber, pyrotechnics, vehicles and bedding and there is a railway works complex at Swindon. The M4 Motorway crosses North Wiltshire.

The overall co-ordination for fire prevention is carried out at Brigade HQ through the FP sections at divisional level whose officers make statutory and goodwill inspections.

Wholetime recruits receive initial training at the Hampshire Fire Brigade training school at Eastleigh whilst Wiltshire trains the retained recruits at either Chippenham or Trowbridge and other courses including BA and driving are carried out at Brigade level.

The Brigade vehicle workshops are at Trowbridge although routine maintenance and services can be carried out at Salisbury workshops.

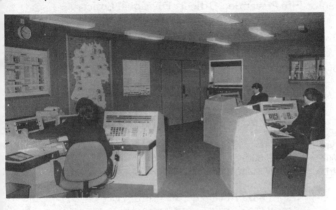

For many years the pumping appliance fleet consisted of HCB-Angus/Bedford TKs and a number of these remain. More recently Dodge K850, K1113 and G1313 appliances with a variety of body makes have been operated and last year three Dennis SS WrL/Rs were commissioned.

The Brigade has two TLs (Dodge/Carmichael/Magirus & AEC Mecury/Merryweather) and four ETs (2 Dodge/Merryweather and one each Dodge/Carmichael & Range Rover/Carmichael). The CU/CaV is a Dodge with Benson bodywork. A number of Land Rover 109s are used as L4Vs and an ex Home Office Bedford R BL is used on workshops.

First away pumps on all stations carry full rescue equipment and are classed as WrL/R.

Photographs on this and the previous two pages show the Headquarters building at Manor House, Potterne, Devizes and outside and inside the new Control Room.

PRINCIPAL OFFICERS

Chief Fire Officer: D.F. Robins Esq., QFSM, FIFireE
      Deputy Chief Fire Officer: K.G. Monk Esq., MIFireE
Third Officer/Senior Staff Officer: Senior Divisional Officer
      M.G. Tatem, MIFireE
Senior Fire Prevention Officer: Divisional Officer
      C.R. Mosely, MIFireE
Divisional Commander North Division (Swindon):
      Divisional Officer J.H. Herrick, MIFireE, MBIM
Divisional Commander South Division (Salisbury):
      Divisional Officer D.W. England, MIFireE

RESERVE APPLIANCES etc:

Type	Reg. No.	Make	Body	Station	Ex.
WrL	KMW 890P	Dodge K850	Carmichael	T/Sch.	1/4
WrL	VMW 512K	Bedford TK	HCB-Angus	4/1	1/6 & 1/5
WrL	SMW 657J	Bedford TK	HCB-Angus	1/1	3/3
WrL	SMW 659J	Bedford TK	HCB-Angus	4/1	2/1
WrL	PHR 589H	Bedford TK	HCB-Angus	4/1	2/3
WrL	PHR 590H	Bedford TK	HCB-Angus	3/1	4/6
WrL	PHR 591H	Bedford TK	HCB-Angus	4/1	3/1 & 3/5
L4V	JMW 783P	Land Rover			
GPV(DI)	MMR 600R	Dodge K1113	Jones & Bence	4/6	
BL	372 ALC	Bedford R	Home Office	4/1	
PE	HMR 765	Dennis F12	Dennis	1/1 museum	3/1

Photographs on opposite page show (top to bottom): Workshops at 4/1 with former 1/5 WrL JWV 895F (Bedford TK/CHB-Angus) now pres. by World Wildlife Butterfly Farm near Sherborne; Spare WrLs JAM 374F (withdrawn) & PHR 589H (both Bedford TK/HCB-Angus) at 4/1; spare WrL PHR 591H & L4V DWV 260L (3/1) at 2/1.

Drove Road, Swindon.   Risk: B — D
Est: 76 — 71 W/T (1 A.D.O., 4 Stn.O., 4 Sub.O., 8 Lfm., 54 Fm.)
          5 R/T (1 Lfm., 4 Fm.)

O.i/c: A.D.O. McGill   Av. call: 1,300.   Pop:130,000

60 sq. m. large fast growing North Wiltshire town and surrounding
rural area; purpose built Brunel Centre shopping precinct, commercial
area and housing estates with some high rise buildings. Heavy and light
industry on factory estates with warehousing and railway works
complex. 5 hospitals and numerous old peoples homes. M4 Motorway.
Military establishments.

WrL/R	RMW 21 Y	Dennis SS/Perkins	Dennis
WrL	YMW 63V	Dodge G1313/Perkins	HCB-Angus
WrL	OMR 703M	Dodge K850/Perkins	Carmichael (ex. 4/1)
ET	PMR 713M	Dodge K850/Perkins	Merryweather
TL	XMW 758T	Dodge G1690/Perkins	Carmichael/Magirus
L4V	A53 RWS	Land Rover (d).	

Works FB at British Rail and RAF & RN FBs at Wroughton (hospital
& helicopters).

Preserved PE HMR 765 (Dennis FI2 ex. Wilts. FB 3/1) in Brigade
museum at 1/1. J.V. Brownlee owns 1962 Morris CU/RU 882 NWL
(ex Nuffield Exports, Cowley). M. Walker & R. Palmer own 1957
Dennis/Rolls OMR 818 (ex. Westinghouse works FB, Chippenham).
Station picture incls. WrL GHR 619N now at 1/5.

Bath Road, Cricklade.   Risk: D

Est. 11 — (1 Stn.O., 2 Lfm., 8 Fm.)

O.i/c: Stn.O. Collier   Av. call: 100.   Pop: 20,000

50 sq. m. small North Wiltshire town and surrounding villages. Mainly agricultural with some light industry. Numerous old peoples homes & boarding school. Military establishments. Large area of open water (gravel pits). Covering o.t.b. into Gloucestershire.

WrL/R   KMW 891P   Dodge K850/Perkins Carmichael (ex 2/1)

Picture below shows 1/1 TL.

High Street, Ramsbury.　　　　　　　　　Risk: D

Est: 12 — (1 Stn.O., 2 Lfm., 9 Fm.)

O.i/c:　Stn.O. Mills.　　　　　　Av. call: 75.　　　　　Pop: 7,000

50 sq. m. small North East Wiltshire town and neighbouring villages.
Mainly rural with agriculture and forestry plantation on edge of
Savernake Forest. Light industry & several large country mansions.

WrL/R	CMW 687L	Dodge K850/Perkins	HCB-Angus (ex.1/1)
L4V	BHR 459B	Land Rover	Carmichael (ex. 1/1 DU)

Preserved Hadley, Simpkin & Lott manual with Tilley pump (approx.
1770) at station.

Station photograph includes L4V 15 BMR since withdrawn.

Picture below shows training school WrL KMW 890P (ex. 1/4).

Highworth Road, Stratton St. Margaret, Swindon.　　　Risk: B – D

Est: 25 – 13 W/T (1 Stn.O., 1 Sub.O., 3 Lfm., 8 Fm.)
　　　　　12 R/T (1 Sub.O., 2 Lfm., 9 Fm.)

O.i/c:　Stn.O. Humphries　　　Av. call: 450　　　Pop:25,000

60 sq. m. North East suburbs of Swindon and rural area including Highworth. Heavy and light industry (incl. British Leyland) in four industrial estates. Works airfield, geriatric hospital and M4 Motorway. Covering o.t.b. into Oxfordshire.

WrL/R	RMW 23Y	Dennis SS/Perkins	Dennis
WrL	OHR 622R	Dodge K1113/Perkins	ERF Fire Fighter
L4V	EHR 125C	Land Rover	

Works FBs at British Leyland (Commer WrT & u/van) & Vickers Airfield (L4P with dry powder unit).

Photograph of station includes WrL KMV 890P (Dodge/Carmichael) now at Brigade Training School).

Pictures below show Dennis SS WrL/R 1/1 (left) and 1/4 (right).

The Parade, Marlborough.　　　　　　Risk: C & D.
Est: 20 — (1 Stn.O., 1 Sub.O., 4 Lfm., 14 Fm.)

O.i/c:　Stn.O. Pike　　　　　Av. call: 200　　　　Pop: 20,000

70 sq. m. medium sized mid Wiltshire town and surrounding villages.
Commercial centre of large area of rural Wiltshire, has many Georgian
buildings. Light industry and agriculture; Marlborough College; large
area of Forestry plantation in Savernake Forest. Savernake Cottage
Hospital (gen.) & children's hospital.

WrL/R　　　KMW 889P　Dodge K850/Perkins　Carmichael
WrL　　　　GHR 619N　Dodge K850/Perkins　HCB-Angus (ex. 1/1)
Station photograph shows WrL VMW 512K (Bedford/HCB-Angus)
now reserve at 4/1.

Picture below shows Dennis F12 PE HMR 76S (ex. 3/1 preserved by
W.F.B. at 1/1) at FSNBF rally, Blandford (17/7/83).

Station Road, Wootton Bassett. Risk: C & D

Est: 11 — (1 Stn.O., 2 Lfm., 8 Fm.)

O.i/c: Stn.O. Taylor Av. Call: 160 Pop:12,000

40 sq. m. small North Wiltshire town with considerable residential development, and surrounding villages in rural area. Light industry includes dairy production complex. RAF Lyneham (transport base). M4 Motorway.

WrL/R GMW 180W Dodge G1313/Perkins CFE

RAF Fire Service at Lyneham with crash & foam tenders and RIVs.

Lfm Wannell (1/6) owns 1942 Austin 60' TL (GXN 205) ex. Somerset FB 02 Bridgwater & 01 Taunton pictured below.

Dallas Road, Chippenham.   Risk: C & D

Est: 27 — 7 W/T (1 Stn.O., 1 Sub.O., 1 Lfm. 4 Fm.)
        20 R/T (1 Sub.O., 4 Lfm., 15 Fm.)

O.i/c: Stn.O. Robinson.   Av. call: 400.   Pop: 26,000

75 sq. m. medium sized market town and surrounding villages; several industrial sites of varying risks. Large rural area with agriculture. Four hospitals and several old peoples homes. M4 Motorway.

WrL/R	MHR 849X	Dodge G1313/Perkins	HCB-Angus
WrL	WWV 947K	Bedford TK	HCB-Angus (ex. 1/2)
ET	KMR 673P	Range Rover	Carmichael
CU/CaV	NAM 262X	Dodge GO9/Perkins	Benson
L4V	JHR 485E	Land Rover	

Picture below shows 2/1 CU/CaV and 3/1 ET at scene of fire Stoby's Restaurant, Butcher's Row, Salisbury (6/7/82).

Beachfield Road, Corsham.   Risk: C & D
Est: 19 — (1 Stn.O., 1 Sub.O., 4 Lfm., 13 Fm.)
O.i/c: Stn.O. Hancock.   Av. call: 180.   Pop:12,000
45 sq. m small West Wiltshire town on edge of Cotswolds. Light industry
including 2 rubbers works. Villages in surrounding rural area with
agriculture & Forestry plantation. Military & government establishments.

WrL/R	XMW 61V	Dodge G1313/Perkins	HCB-Angus
WrL	SMW 660J	Bedford TK	HCB-Angus

RAF Fire Service at Rudloe Manor with Bedford WrT.
Two pres. manual pumps (early 19th century) - Hadley & Simpkin
and Merryweather at 2/2.
Station picture shows L4V FMW 702D now at 2/4 Calne.
Picture below shows 2/1 ET.

Gloucester Road, Malmesbury.　　　　　　　　Risk: C & D

Est: 11 — (1 Sub.O., 2 Lfm., 8 Fm.)

O.i/c:　Stn.O. Bates.　　　　　　Av. call: 150.　　　　　Pop: 7,500

95 sq. m. small North West Wiltshire and surrounding villages in large rural area on edge of the Cotswolds. Light industry and agriculture. Home for severely handicapped children. M4 Motorway. RAF establishments.

WrL/R	YMW 62V	Dodge G1313/Perkins HCB-Angus
L4V	FMW 703D	Land Rover

RAF FS at Hullavington.

Barr family own pres. Austin ATV GXH 682 (ex. Home Office in London & Gloucestershire FS).

Picture below shows 2/1 CU.

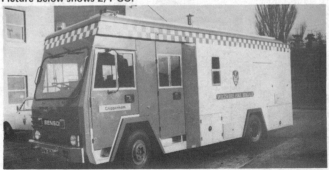

Station Road, Calne.   Risk: C & D

Est: 12 — (1 Sub.O., 2 Lfm., 9 Fm.)

O.1/c: Sub.O. Nott.   Av. call: 150.   Pop: 14,000

70 sq. m. small mid Wiltshire market town on A4 trunk road and surrounding villages in large rural area on edge of Marlborough Downs. Light industry, agriculture and Forestry plantation.

WrL/R   UMW 329T   Dodge K1113/Perkins CFE
L4V   FMW 702D   Land Rover

Picture below shows driving instruction vehicle at 4/6.

Ashley Road, Salisbury.   Risk: B — D

Est: 65 — 45 W/T (1 A.D.O., 4 Sub.O., 8 Lfm., 32 Fm.)
      20 R/T (2 Sub.O., 4 Lfm., 14 Fm.)

O.i/c: A.D.O. Humphries.   Av. call: 600.   Pop: 70,000

100 sq. m. cathedral city in South East Wiltshire and large rural area with numerous villages. City centre & market place formed of old half-timbered prop. but with modern shopping precinct. Several industrial estates with varied industries including pyrotechnists. Many thatch prop. & large farms. Salisbury Cathedral, 4 hospitals (gen. ment., hand. & ger.), CD & military establishments & works airfield.

WrL/R	RMW 22Y	Dennis SS/Perkins	Dennis
WrL	YMW 64V	Dodge G1313/Perkins	HCB-Angus
WrL	CMW 688L	Dodge K850/Perkins	HCB-Angus
TL	MMR 217G	AEC Mercury	Merryweather
ET	GHR 618N	Dodge K850/Perkins	Merryweather
L4V	A352 SFB	Land Rover (d)	
L4V	DWV 260L	Land Rover	
L4V	BHR 460B	Land Rover	Carmichael (ex. DU)

Works FB at Pains-Wessex (WrT-776 RYD ex. Somerset - Pill - Bedford TJ/HCB-Angus; P-JMW 424 ex. Wiltshire 2/4, 2/3 & 1/1 Dennis F8); works FB at Edgley Ltd., Old Sarum Airfield (WrT — ETK 562D ex. Dorset (A3) Bedford TJ/HCB-Angus); MOB FB at CDE Porton Down with P, WrC & L4P.

Mr. R. Brown owns: pres. ex. Wilts (3/2) WrT YWV 913 (Bedford TK/HCB-Angus); ex. Tisbury FB HRT CAM 711 (Dennis/New World) & Dennis TA tr. pump; ex. Somerset (Yeovil) TL GXN 208 (Austin K4); ex. City of Oxford WrT 959 KJO (Karrier Gamecock/Carmichael) latterly Listers, Dursley, Glos.

Wiltshire FB own pres. PE HMR 765 (Dennis F12) ex. 3/1 now at 1/1.

Mr. R. Bone (Botley) owns ex. 3/1 WrT VAM 828 (Bedford/Miles).

Station picture includes former res. WrT (ex. 3/5) EMW 684D (Bedford TK/HCB-Angus) now at Airsprung, Trowbridge.

Minster Street, Wilton.   Risk: C & D

Est: 10 — (1 Stn.O., 2 Lfm., 7 Fm.)

O.i/c: Sub.O. Perry.   Av. call: 120.   Pop: 14,000

90 sq. m. small South Wiltshire town and surrounding villages in large rural area. Light industry including carpet weaving and felt production. Farmland & Forestry plantation. Wilton House stately home; Army establishment (U.K. Land Forces H.Q.).

WrL/R   SAM 187S   Dodge K1113/Perkins Angloco

Pres. Newham hand drawn pump (circ. 1720) under renovation at 3/2.

Picture below shows works FB appliances at Pains-Wessex and pres. ex. 3/2 WrT YMV 913.

The Avenue, Tisbury.　　　　　　　Risk: D

Est: 13 — (1 Stn.O., 2 Lfm., 10 Fm.)

O.i/c:　Stn.O. Smart.　　　　　Av. call: 90.　　　　Pop: 5,000

90 sq. m. small South Wiltshire town and surrounding villages in large rural area. Light industry, farmland, heathland and Forestry plantation. MOD establishments.

WrL/R　　　OHR 623R　　Dodge K1113/Perkins　ERF Fire-fighter
　　　　　　　　　　　　　　　　　　　　　　　　(ex. 3/5)

RAF Fire Service with Bedford/Carmichael WrTs at Chilmark and Baverstock.

Picture below shows ex 3/3 Dennis New World HRT CAM 711 and Dennis TA tr. pump (pres. Roger Brown, Salisbury).

White Road, Mere.   Risk: D

Est: 12 — (1 Stn.O., 2 Lfm., 9 Fm.)

O.i/c: Stn.O. Howell.   Av. call: 80.   Pop: 5,500

100 sq. m. small South West Wiltshire town and surrounding villages. Mainly rural with light industry, agriculture and Forestry plantation. Covering o.t.b. into Dorset and Somerset.

WrL/R   UMW 328T   Dodge K1113/Perkins   CFE

Mr. K.C. Spencer of St. Martin's Farm, Zeals owns ex. Wiltshire FB WrTs: KMR 388 (Commer/Miles ex. 1/1 and 2/2) & BHR 369B (Bedford/HCB-Angus ex. 3/1) pictured below.

Salisbury Road, Amesbury. Risk: C & D

Est: 26 — 6 W/T (1 Sub.O., 1 Lfm., 4 Fm.)
    20 R/T (1 Sub.O., 4 Lfm., 15 Fm.)

O.i/c: A.D.O. Humphries (3/1). Av. call: 250. Pop:12,000

120 sq. m. medium sized country town in middle of Salisbury Plain. Light industry and agriculture in extensive rural area. Numerous military establishments including airfield and helicopter base and large NAFFI warehouse. Open heathland on army ranges.

| WrL/R | MHR 850X | Dodge G1313/Perkins | HCB-Angus |
| WrL | VMW 513K | Bedford TK | HCB-Angus (ex. 3/4) |

Army FS at Netheravon with CrTs & L4Ps and MOD FB at Boscombe Down with CrTs, RIVs etc.

Picture below shows 3/1 WrL YMW 64V in maintenance bay 3/1.

Castle Street, Ludgershall.   Risk: D

Est: 12 – (1 Stn.O., 2 Lfm., 9 Fm.)

O.i/c: Stn.O. Beard.   Av. call: 150.   Pop: 14,000

70 sq. m. small East Wiltshire town on edge of Salisbury Plain with neighbouring villages and military garrison town of Tidworth. Mostly rural with light industry, agriculture and Forestry plantation. Numerous MOD establishments and army ranges on open heathland. Covering o.t.b. into Hampshire.

WrL/R   UMW 326T   Dodge K1113/Perkins CFE

Station picture includes L4V 16 BMR (now withdrawn).

Picture below shows 3/1 ET.

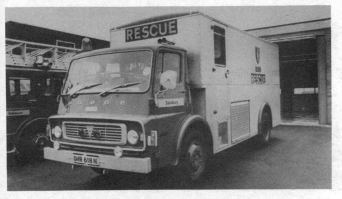

North Street, Pewsey.   Risk: D

Est: 12 — (1 Stn.O., 2 Lfm., 9Fm.)

O.i/c: Sub.O. Wiltshire.   Av. call: 110.   Pop: 9,000

60 sq. m. small town on North East side of Salisbury Plain. Several small villages in rural area with light industry and farmland. Mental hospital. MOD establishments includes airfield and army ranges on open heathland.

WrL/R   SAM 186S   Dodge K1113/Perkins Angloco

RAF Fire Service at Upavon with Bedford WrTs and Dennis CrT.

Former 3/7 Fm. Mr. C. New owns preserved Merryweather Valiant steam fire pump (approx. 1915) ex. ministry of defence.

Picture below shows 3/1 TL.

Hilperton Road, Trowbridge.   Risk: C & D

Est: 29 — 13 W/T (1 Stn.O., 1 Sub.O., 2 Lfm., 9 Fm.)
        16 R/T (1 Sub.O., 2 Lfm., 12 Fm.)

O.i/c: Stn.O. Harris.   Av. call: 400.   Pop: 40,000

45 sq. m. medium sized West Wiltshire county town and surrounding villages. Formerly a centre of weaving trade; expanding light industry now includes bedding manuf. and breweries. Rural area with Forestry plantation and farming. General hospital. Covering o.t.b. into Somerset.

WrL/R	GMW 182W	Dodge G1313/Perkins	CFE
WrL	CMW 686L	Dodge K850/Perkins	HCB-Angus
ET	FHR 622W	Dodge S56	Carmichael
L4V	JHR 486E	Land Rover	

Four WrLs are kept at Brigade W/S, Trowbridge (see earlier list).

Works FB at Airsprung with ex. Wiltshire FB WrT EMW 684D (Bedford TK/HCB-Angus ex. 3/5; see 3/1).

Picture below shows former WrT RHT 553 (Bedford SL/HCB ex. Bristol now pres. see Avon FB).

Station Approach, Bradford-on-Avon.   Risk: C & D

Est: 11 — (1 Stn.O., 2 Lfm., 8 Fm.)

O.i/c: Sub.O. Myatt.   Av. call: 150.   Pop: 12,000

50 sq. m. small West Wiltshire town built on side of hill making access difficult to some properties. A number of small villages in Limpley Stoke Valley. Agriculture & light industry including rubber manuf. Covering o.t.b. into Avon & Somerset.

WrL/R   SAM 188S   Dodge K1113/Perkins Angloco

Works FB at Avon Rubber, Bradford-on-Avon with Austin Gypsy L4P. Pres. Shand Mason escape ladder (approx. 1900) ex. Bradford-on-Avon at station).

Picture below shows ex. 3/1 WrT (1959) VAM 828 (Bedford/Miles) pres. by Mr. R. Bone (Botley, Hants).

Semington Road, Melksham.   Risk: C & D

Est: 12 – (1 Stn.O. 2 Lfm., 9 Fm.)

O.i/c: Stn.O. Quadling.   Av. call: 180.   Pop:16,000

60 sq. m. medium sized West Wiltshire industrial town and surrounding villages. Light industry including rubber manuf. Rural area with agriculture & Forestry plantation.

WrL/R   UMW 327T   Dodge K1113/Perkins Carmichael

Works FB at Avon Rubber, Melksham with WrT OMW 962M (Bedford TK/HCB-Angus), L2P BHR 607L (Ford Transit) & DCU PAM 248R (Ford A0610/G & T Attack, ex. Westinghouse Works FB).

Station picture includes reserve WrT SMW 659J (ex. 4/6).

Meadow Lane, Westbury.   Risk: C & D

Est: 12 — (1 Sub.O., 2 Lfm., 9 Fm.)

O.i/c: Sub.O. Stott.   Av. call: 120.   Pop: 12,000

50 sq. m. small West Wiltshire market town bordering Salisbury Plain, noted for mid Georgean architecture. Rural area includes several villages, numerous farms and Forestry plantation. Light industry on trading estates and extensive railway sidings. MOD establishments with army firing ranges on open heathland. General hospital.

WrL/R   GMW 181W   Dodge G1313/Perkins CFE

Picture below shows 4/1 ET.

Portway, Warminster.   Risk: D

Est: 20 — (1 Stn.O., 1 Sub.O., 4 Lfm., 14 Fm.)

O.i/c: Stn.O. Francis.   Av. call: 170.   Pop: 17,000

120 sq. m. medium sized West Wiltshire town bordering Salisbury Plain with mid Georgean architecture. Light industry includes shoe & glove manuf. Extensive rural area with several villages, farming and Forestry plantation. Numerous MOD establishments with army firing ranges on open heathland. Gen. hospital, public school and Longleat House.

WrL/R	GHR 617N	Dodge K850/Perkins	Carmichael
WrT	VMW 511K	Bedford TK	HCB-Angus
L4V	FMW 704D	Land Rover	

Picture below shows W/S BL 372 ALC (often garaged at 4/5).

Southbroom Road, Devizes.   Risk: C & D

Est: 20 (1 Stn.O., 1 Sub.O., 4 Lfm., 14 Fm.)

O.i/c: Stn.O. Flowers.   Av. call: 270.   Pop: 16,000

80 sq. m. medium sized mid Wiltshire town on North side of Salisbury Plain. Numerous villages in large rural area. Light industry, farming and Forestry plantation. Army firing ranges on open heathland. Roundway Hospital.

WrL/R	OHR 621 R	Dodge K1113/Perkins	ERF Fire-fighter
WrL	PHR 603M	Dodge K850/Perkins	Carmichael (ex. 3/1)
L4V	EHR 124C	Land Rover	(ex. 4/1).

Station picture shows Reserve WrT PHR 590H (3/1).

Picture below shows L4Vs , 4/5 and 4/6 at 4/1.

GLOUCESTERSHIRE FIRE AND RESCUE SERVICE

The Gloucestershire Fire and Rescue Service received its title in 1982 after 34 years as the Gloucestershire Fire Service.

The local government reorganisation of 1974 resulted in the county losing five stations, Thornbury, Yate, Patchway, Kingswood and Severnside to the new county of Avon.

The City of Gloucester Fire Brigade had previously, in 1972, combined with the county brigade which now consists of 20 stations in two divisions, West and East. All the stations, except one, were built since 1950; three are whole-time, one day-manning and the rest retained.

A retained station at Chipping Sodbury closed soon after a new D/M station at Yate opened in 1969. The City of Gloucester closed two stations when a new station was opened in 1956. Plans for completely new stations at Berkeley (Dursley) and Bishop's Cleeve (Cheltenham) were shelved.

Headquarters and workshops are based along with the East Division H.Q., at a purpose built complex, which also includes the fire station, at Cheltenham. The West Division is centered on Gloucester.

The county is mainly D risk though B risk areas exist in the commercial and industrial parts of Gloucester, Cheltenham and Stroud, whilst the built up areas of Cirencester, Tewkesbury, Dursley, Coleford and Lydney rate as C risk.

Fire control at Cheltenham deals with an average of 5,000 calls a year and uses the V.F.A. system for turnouts whilst the Brigade is in the process of introducing new multi-tone alerters.

Plans are well advanced for the commissioning of a new

computer-assisted mobilising and communications system in September 1984, working in conjunction with the Home Office radio scheme to carry speech and data to the Brigade's 16 retained stations. A new control room is being developed in the existing East Division building.

The Brigade training department is based at Headquarters which organises a variety of internal courses.

Training efficiency is monitored each year on risk exercises with marks awarded to stations for leadership, command, firemanship, breathing apparatus and radio procedure. Wholetime, retained and youth quizzes are organised.

Overall policy and co-ordination of FP work is carried out by the Senior Fire Precautions Officer (DOI), assisted by a staff officer (ADO), at the Brigade H.Q., whilst the day to day administration is decentralised to Divisional level.

Much of Gloucestershire is rural with the Forest of Dean in the West and the scarplands of the Cotswolds in the East separated by the River Severn which widens into a tidal estuary below Gloucester with a noted dock area at Sharpness.

The main centres of population are Gloucester, noted for its historic cathedral, and the fashionable spa of Cheltenham.

Industries vary from heavy engineering, plastics and electronics to timber and woollen. The M5 Motorway follows the Severn Valley and there is a commercial airport at Staverton as well as military airfields.

For a number of years the county's fleet of front line appliances consisted of Ford/HCB-Angus WrLs and WrTs. During the 1978/9 period six Bedford/Merryweather appliances were purchased followed by six Bedford/CFEs in 1979/80. In 1983 six Dodge/Carmichael appliances went on the run and most of the early Ford D600s were sold. Recently Dennis D WrL at Wotton-Under-Edge and the county's two Ford/HCB-Angus PEs have been replaced, although the PEs have been retained for training purposes.

The fleet's special appliances include two HPs (a new re-chassied Dodge/Carmichael/Simon and an ERF/HCB-Angus/Simon) three Ford A0610 vans as control-unit, foam carrier and salvage tender, and a Dodge CIU. The emergency rescue appliances consist of a Ford/Bates complete with Dial-Homes '750' twin-boom wrecker, and a Dodge 50/Carmichael.

PRINCIPAL OFFICERS

Chief Fire Officer: R.G. Wilson Esq., GIFireE
Deputy Chief Fire Officer: M.A. Lambourne Esq., MIFireE
Third Officer/Senior Staff Officer: Senior Divisional Officer:
    J. Nash, MIFireE
Senior Fire-Prevention Officer: Divisional Officer P.J. Rose
Divisional Commander West Division (Gloucester):
    Divisional Officer G. Jackson MIFireE
Divisional Commander East Division (Cheltenham):
    Divisional Officer B.J. Cook

RESERVE APPLIANCES etc:

Type	Reg. No.	Make	Body	Ex.
WrT/WrL	LDG 296F	Ford D600	HCB-Angus	22
WrT/WrL	WDF 803J	Ford D600	HCB-Angus	07
WrT/WrL	WDF 804J	Ford D600	HCB-Angus	10
WrT/WrL	WDF 805J	Ford D600	HCB-Angus	02
WrT/WrL	WDF 807J	Ford D600	HCB-Angus	08
PE (DI)	EAD 958L	Ford D1013	HCB-Angus	07 & 05
PE (YTS)	DDD 700L	Ford D1013	HCB-Angus	12

YTS = Youth Training Scheme for 20 young people (including two
females). Objectives of training are to develop leadership and citizen-
ship qualities and to instil a sense of discipline and team-work amongst
the group. Trainees gain experience through all departments of the
Fire and Rescue Service.

Pictures previous 2 pages show Brigade Control and W/S with (above)
21 WrL (BDG 476T), 05 WrL (DDF 941T) & new Dodge/Carmichael
WrL (A211 HFN) and below 07 WrL (JFH 320V). This page shows
Brigade HQ.

Hill Street, Lydney.   Risk: C & D

Est: 18 — (1 Stn.O., 1 Sub.O., 4 Lfm., 12 Fm.)

O.i/c: Stn. O. Jones.   Av. call: 175   Pop: 21,000

70 sq. m. Small West Gloucestershire town bordering Forest of Dean by River Severn. Neighbouring villages including Blakeney. Light industry incl. paper mill & plywood factory. Lydney Cottage Hospital (gen.) & 2 homes for ment. hand. Rural area with farming & forestry plantation.

WrL	EAD 952L	Ford D1013	HCB-Angus (ex. 14)
WrT	PDF 831M	Ford D1011	HCB-Angus

Military FB with Tr. pump at Army Apprentices Coll., Beachley.

Station picture includes WrL VDF 862S now at 14.

Picture below shows former HGV Training WrT LDG 293F.

Cinder Hill, Coleford.   Risk: C & D

Est: 17 — (1 Stn.O., 1 Sub.O., 4 Lfm., 11 Fm.)

O.i/c: Stn. O. Barrow.   Av. call: 250   Pop: 7.500

110 sq. m. Small West Glos. town bordering Forest of Dean and surrounding villages. Light industry incl. sawmills and corrugated case manuf., farming, forestry plantation and open commonland. Covering o.t.b. into Gwent.

WrL	JFH 318V	Bedford TKG (d)	CFE (ex. O5)
WrT	JFH 319V	Bedford TKG (d)	CFE (ex. O5)
L4P	SDF 893N	Land Rover 109	Bates

Works FB with L4P at Reed Corrugated Cases, Lydbrook

Picture below shows 05 Gloucester HP.

Belle View Road, Cinderford. Risk: C & D

Est: 18 — (1 Stn.O., 1 Sub.O., 4 Lfm., 12 Fm.)

O.i/c; Stn. O. Warren-Edwards Av. call: 250 Pop: 14,000

80 sq. m. Small West Glos. town bordering Forest of Dean and surrounding villages incl. Mitcheldean and Newnham. Major and light industries incl. metal refiners and photocopying machine manuf., farming, forestry plantation and open commonland. Dilke Hospital (gen.) and spec. schools..

WrL	BDG 943K	Ford D1013	HCB-Angus
WrT	EAD 956L	Ford D1013	HCB-Angus
L4V	JDF 992N	Land Rover 109	(ex. O5)

Works FBs at Englhards (metal ref.), Cinderford with ex. Glos (12) WrT (WDF 805J — Ford D600 HCB-Angus) and pictured below Rank-Xerox (photocopiers), Mitcheldean with ex. Glos (07) WrL (DDF 454E — Ford D600 HCB-Angus) & ex. Staffordshire WrT (KFA 704 — Bedford TJ5 HCB).

Station Road, Newent.   Risk: D

Est: 12 — (1 Sub.O., 2 Lfm., 9 Fm.)

O.i/c: Sub. O. Bowers.   Av. call: 200   Pop: 10,000

100 sq. m. Small North West Glos. town with large surrounding rural area incl. several villages. Light industry inc. saw-mills: forestry plant-ation and open commonland. M50 Motorway. Covering o.t.b. into Hereford & Worcester.

WrL   EAD 957L   Ford D1013   HCB-Angus

Fire Station building shared with Gloucestershire Ambulance Service.
Picture below shows CU/CAV at 05 Gloucester.

Eastern Avenue, Gloucester.   Risk: B, C, D.
Est: 74 — 52 W/T (1 A.D.O., 1 Stn.O., 4 Sub.O., 8 Lfm., 48 Fm.)
         12 R/T (1 Sub.O., 2 Lfm., 9 Fm.)

O.i/c: A.D.O. Murgatroyd   Av. Call: 1,450   Pop: 100,000

90 sq. m. Large city with covered pedestrian modern shop. precinct within older styled city centre shop. area. Dense res., comm. and indust. areas incl. warehousing, chemical works, cold storage & refrig. plant and petrol storage depot. Cathedral, prison & old dock area part of which under reconstruction for leisure purposes. Gloucestershire Royal (gen.) & Coney Hill (ment.) & Horton Road (ment.) Hospitals. M5 Motorway. Large storage depot at R.A.F. Quedgeley. Staverton Airport (comerc.).

WrL	BDG 42Y	Dodge G13C/Perkins	Carmichael
WrL	DDF 941T	Bedford TKG (d)	CFE (ex. 07)
WrT	CFH 661Y	Dodge G13C/Perkins	Carmichael
HP	OFH 999F	ERF 84RS/Rolls Royce	HCB-Angus/Simon
CU/CaV	HFN 671N	Ford A0610	

RAF FS at Quedgeley with WrT & Airport FB at Staverton. Works FB (picture below) at Glos. Trading Estate, Hucclecote with L4P (Land Rover 88/Miles, 9290 DD).

M.T. Williams of Barnwood owns pres. ex. Bootle Dennis F8 Pump (EM 5512) & Commer/Miles ET (EM 6210).

Station picture includes spare WrL LDG 296F.

Pullens Road, Painswick.   Risk: D

Est: 9 — (1 Sub.O., 2 Lfm., 6 Fm.)

O.i/c: Sub. O. Perrins.   Av. call: 80   Pop:6,000

70 sq. m. Medium sized mid Cotswold village and surrounding villages.
Mostly rural with farming , commonland and woodland. Several large
country houses; two homes for mentally handicapped.

WrT   BDG 941K   Ford D1013   HCB-Angus

(Police house next door).

Picture below shows Stn. 07 ERA.

Paganhill Lane, Stroud.   Risk: B, C, D.
Est: 53 — 41 W/T (1 A.D.O., 4 Sub.O., 4 Lfm., 32 Fm.)
       12 R/T (1 Sub.O., 2 Lfm, 9 Fm.)

O.i/c: A.D.O. Martin   Av. call: 650   Pop: 30,000

100 sq. m. Medium sized mid Cotswold town and surrounding villages incl. Stonehouse and Chalford — ground extends to River Severn. Shopping precinct, heavy and light industry incl. engineering works and woollen mills. Stroud General, Stroud Maternity and Standish (gen.). Hospitals and several homes for elderly. Farming, open commonland and woodland.

WrL	BDG 39Y	Dodge G1313/Perkins	Carmichael
WrT	JFH 320V	Bedford TKG (d)	CFE
ERA	JHY 616X	Dodge 50	Carmichael
CIU	CDG 998Y	Dodge G75C/Perkins	Rollalongs/Benson
FoC/TV	CAD 319T	Ford A0610	
L4V	JDF 991N	Land Rover 109	

Station picture includes spare WrL WDF 804J.

Old Market, Nailsworth.   Risk: D

Est: 15 — (1 Stn.O., 1 Sub.O., 3 Lfm., 10 Fm.)

O.i/c: Stn. O. Beale   Av. call: 160   Pop: 10,000

70 sq. m. Small South Cotswold market town with six surrounding villages. Steep wooded hills with various light industrial sites in valleys. Two residential schools for ment. hand. Large M.O.D. store and air-field. Royal residence at Gatcombe Park.

WrL	PDG 664G	Ford D600	HCB-Angus (ex. 14)
WrT	EAD 995L	Ford D1013	HCB-Angus

M.O.D. Fire Service at Aston Down with L4P.

Picture below shows O7 CIU.

Symn Lane, Wotton-Under-Edge.   Risk: D

Est: 9 — (1 Sub.O., 2 Lfm., 6 Fm.)

O.i/c: Sub. O. Durn   Av. call: 100   Pop: 6,500

50 sq. m. Small South Cotswold market town and several surrounding villages. Mostly rural with light industry incl. elastic weaving. Farming, commonland and forestry plantation. Covering o.t.b. into Avon.

WrL   PDF 833M   Ford D1011   HCB-Angus (ex. 21)

Station picture shows former WrL JFH 958K (Dennis D/Jaguar) now withdrawn and sold to Listers Diesels, Dursley.

Picture below shows 12 ST/TV.

Castle Street, Dursley.   Risk: C & D

Est: 17 — (1 Stn.O., 1 Sub.O., 4 Lfm., 11 Fm.)

O.1/c: Stn.O. Allen   Av. call: 200   Pop: 8,000

100 sq. m. Small South Cotswold town and surrounding villages. Light industry incl. diesel engine manuf. Sharpness Docks and Berkeley Nuclear Power Station. Rural area with farming, commonland and woodland. M5 Motorway.

WrL	EAD 954L	Ford D1013	HCB-Angus (ex. 18)
WrT	EAD 953L	Ford D1013	HCB-Angus

Works FBs at C.E.G.B. Berkeley with PFoT & at Listers Diesels, Dursley (below) with WrL JFH 958K (ex. Glos. 05 & 09 Dennis D/Jaguar), L4P XDD 838S (1970 Land Rover 110/Merryweather) & RT XDD 839S (1969 Austin A55). Picture includes former WrL 959 KJO (ex. 1959 Oxford City Karrier Gamecock/Carmichael) now pres. by R. Brown, Salisbury.

10 Station picture includes former WrL WDF 804J (Ford D600/ HCB-Angus) now a spare.

Keynsham Road, Cheltenham.   Risk: B, C, D.
Est: 74 — 62 W/T (1 A.D.O., 1 Stn.O., 1 Sub.O., 8 Lfm., 48 Fm.)
        12 R/T (1 Sub.O., 2 Lfm., 9 Fm.)

O.i/c: A.D.O. Drew.   Av. call: 1,200   Pop: 120,000

100 sq. m. Large spa town in central Gloucestershire renowned for its
Regency architecture. Heavily populated with shop. centres and
department stores. Light industry incl. various engineering works.
Surrounding area includes Bishop's Cleve and numerous villages,
Cheltenham General & St. Paul's Maternity Hospitals, Cheltenham
Colleges. National Coal Board est. at Stoke Orchard. M5 Motorway.

WrL	BDG 38Y	Dodge G1313/Perkins	Carmichael
WrL	DDF 940T	Bedford TKG (d)	CFE
WrT	BDG 40Y	Dodge G1313/Perkins	Carmichael
HP	A796 FDG	Dodge G16C/Perkins	Carmichael/Simon (re-chassied) 85'
ERA	GDG 559N	Ford DT2417	Bates/Holmes
ST/TV	GFH 951V	Ford A0610	Hicks

Works FBs at Smith Industries, Bishop's Cleve with L2P (Bedford CF)
& Dowty-Rotol Ltd. (below) with L4P (Land Rover 109/Fire Armour,
4292 DD).

Oldbury Road, Tewkesbury. Risk: B, C, D.

Est: 19 — (1 Stn.O., 1 Sub.O., 4 Lfm., 13 Fm.)

O.i/c: Stn. O. King Av. call: 250 Pop: 15,000

70 sq. m. Medium sized North Gloucestershire town and neighbouring villages. Light industry including flour mill and large factory complex at Ashchurch. Rural area with farming. Tewkesbury General Hospital and Tredington Hospital (ger.), Tewkesbury Abbey. M5 and M50 Motorways. Covering o.t.b. into Hereford and Worcester.

WrL	VDF 864S	Bedford TKG (d)	Merryweather
WrT	VDF 862S	Bedford TKG (d)	Merryweather (ex.01)

In March 1983 Tewkesbury Fire Station, built in 1962 (pictured below) and the Ambulance Station (pictured above) exchanged premises. Both are in Oldbury Road. The former Ambulance Station also incorporated the Auxillary Fire Service Station which, after the A.F.S. was disbanded, was used for training purposes by the Gloucestershire Fire Service until December 1982.

Station pictures include (above) spare WrL WDF 807J and (below) WrL EAD 952L now at 01 Lydney.

Gretton Road, Winchcombe.   Risk: D

Est: 8 (1 sub.O., 2 Lfm., 5 Fm.)

O.i/c: Sub. O. Morley   Av. call: 125   Pop: 10,000

100 sq. m. Small North Cotswold market town and surrounding villages. Mainly rural with farming. Light industry including paper mills. Stately homes.

WrL   BDG 940K   Ford D1013   HCB-Angus

Preserved 18th century manual pump at Sudeley Castle and former Worcester City Morris Commercial pump (1934) being restored by Lfm Petchley (Stn. 15).

Picture below shows Stn. 12 ERA.

Catbrook, Chipping Campden.   Risk: D

Est: 10 – (1 Sub.O., 2 Lfm., 7 Fm.)

O.i/c: Sub. O. Brotherton   Av. call: 50   Pop: 7,000

60 Sq. m. Small North Cotswold town and surrounding villages on Gloucestershire, Warwickshire and Hereford and Worcester borders. Light industry, rural area with farming and woodland. Several large country houses.

WrL   DDF 942T   Bedford TKG (d) CFE (ex.12 and 18)

Station picture shows WrL VDF 863S (Bedford TKG/Merryweather) now a WrT at 18 Stow-on-the-Wold.

Picture below shows appliances at Staverton Commercial Airport (05 Gloucester ground).

Parkers Lane, Moreton-in-Marsh. Risk: D

Est: 12 — (1 Sub.O., 2 Lfm., 9 Fm.)

O.i/c: Sub. O. Weller. Av. call: 80 Pop: 8,000

60 sq. m. Small North Cotswold town and neighbouring villages incl. Blockley. Mostly rural with farmland and woodland; light industry incl. paper factory. Several large country houses. Covering o.t.b. into Warwickshire and Oxfordshire.

WrL   VDF 860S   Bedford TKG (d)   Merryweather

Fire Service College at Moreton-in-Marsh (see last section of this booklet).

Also in picture above is spare WrT LDG 294F (now withdrawn).

Picture below shows spare WrT WDF 805J & former PE DDD 700L at North Division HQ.

Union Street, Stow-on-the-Wold.   Risk: D

Est: 18 — (1 Stn.O., 1 Sub.O., 4 Lfm., 12 Fm.)

O.i/c: Stn. O. Arthur.   Av. call: 150   Pop: 15,000

100 sq. m. Small North Cotswold town and surrounding villages incl. Bourton-on-the-Water. Mostly rural with farming and woodland. Light industry incl. brewery. Moore Cottage Hospital. U.S.A.F. airfield at Little Rissington.

WrL	PDF 829M	Ford D1011	HCB-Angus
WrT	VDF 863S	Bedford TKG (d)	Merryweather (ex. 16)

U.S.A.F. brigade at Little Rissington.

Station picture shows WrT (EAD 954L Ford D1013 HCB-Angus) now a WrL at 10 Dursley.

Picture below shows PE (EAD 958L Ford D1013 HCB Angus — ex. O5 and O7) now HGV training appliance.

Oxford Road, Northleach.   Risk: D

Est: 8 — (1 Sub.O., 2 Lfm., 5 Fm.)

O.i/c: Sub O. Holland   Av. call: 50   Pop: 5,000

80 sq. m. Small mid Cotswold town and neighbouring villages. Rural area with farming and several large country houses; forestry plantation, light industry. Northleach Hospital (gen.).

WrT   BDG 673K   Ford D1013   HCB-Angus

Fire Station building shared with Gloucestershire Ambulance Service. **Picture below shows re-chassied HP at 12 Cheltenham.**

Hatherop Road, Fairford.   Risk: D

Est: 11 – (1 Sub.O., 2 Lfm., 8 Fm.)

O.i/c: Sub. O. Cook   Av. call: 100   Pop: 8,500

70 sq. m. Small South Gloucestershire town and surrounding villages.
Rural area with farming, light industry and forestry plantation. U.S.A.F.
airbase (refuelling tanker aircraft). Covering o.t.b. into Wiltshire.

WrT   PDF 832M   Ford D1011   HCB-Angus (ex. 02)

U.S.A.F. brigade at Fairford Airbase.

Station picture shows former WrT (PDF 830M/Ford/HCB-Angus)
destroyed at incident.

**Picture below shows new Dodge G13C/Perkins Carmichael/Riffaud
80' TL (TDA 441Y) for 05 Gloucester.**

Chesterton Lane, Cirencester.　　　　　Risk: C & D

Est: 24 — 13 W/T (1 Stn.O., 2 Sub.O., 2 Lfm., 8 Fm.)
　　　12 R/T (1 Lfm., 9 Fm.)

O.i/c:　Stn. O. Smith.　　　　　Av. call: 300　　　　Pop: 30,000

100 sq. m. Medium sized South Gloucestershire market town with mostly rural area containing some large villages and a number of smaller hamlets. Light industry. Cirencester Memorial (gen.) and Querns Hospitals. R.A.F. airfield at Kemble.

| WrL | BDG 41 Y | Dodge G1313/Perkins | Carmichael |
| WrL | BDG 476T | Bedford TKG (d) | Merryweather |

Royal Air Force FB at Kemble (due to close).

Picture below by Gloucestershire Fire & Rescue Service shows RTA A417 Daglinworth with Ford/HCB-Angus WrT PDF 833M (21 now 09); Summer 1982.

New Church Street, Tetbury.   Risk: D

Est: 11 — (1 Sub.O., 2 Lfm., 8 Fm.)

O.i/c: Sub. O. Dyer   Av. call: 90   Pop: 10,000

70 sq. m. Small South Cotswold town and neighbouring villages. Light industry with warehousing; large farming area, forestry plantations. Tetbury and District Hospitals (gen.) & Cotswold Geriatric Hospital.

WrL   VDF 861S   Bedford TKG (d)   Merryweather

Picture below by Marc Giddings, Gloucestershire County Gazette shows fire at R.A. Lister & Co. Ltd., Dursley with 05 HP; July 1983. Works Fire Station, on left, was not involved in fire.

BERKELEY POWER STATION

The Central Electricity Generating Board has two works brigades and fire stations at Berkeley Power Station; the Laboratory Section (above uses a Leyland Sherpa/Bridge L2P (un-registered) whilst the Power Station has a Dodge S34C/Reeve-Burgess incident vehicle GTC 609X and a Land Rover 109 L4P (with Godiva pump) GKG 188D. Also in the emergency vehicle bays are three Land Rover 109s used for off station non-fire incidents. Other CEGB brigades in this booklet are Hinkley Point (10 Nether Stowey, Somerset) and Oldbury-upon-Severn (A6 Thornbury, Avon).

SOMERSET FIRE BRIGADE

When the Somerset Fire Brigade was formed in 1948 it consisted of 41 stations but by 1970 the number had dropped to 38 with the closure of a retained station at Watchet (Williton) and volunteer stations at Milborne Port (Sherborne) and Wedmore (Cheddar).

With the formation of the new County of Avon in the local government re-organization in 1974, all but one station in Somerset's "A" Division were transferred to the Avon Fire Brigade, thus the present station total is 24 with three W/T and the rest retained.

Since 1953 Headquarters has been situated in a large country mansion "Hestercombe House" at Cheddon Fitzpaine, north of Taunton. Formerly HQ was at Upper High Street, Taunton.

Brigade control is contained in the HQ building and a completely new mobilising system is due to become operational in 1984 using computers and teleprinters with pocket alerters for retained personnel. On average Somerset control handles about 5,000 calls a year.

Also at HQ are the Workshops where the Brigade's recovery vehicle, a Bedford/Wreckers International is stationed.

The Brigade is split into two divisions; the West (11 stations) has Divisional HQ at Taunton whilst Yeovil is HQ of the East (13 stations).

The county is predominately rural with the vast majority 'D' risk. Areas of 'B' risk are in the three major towns of Taunton, Bridgwater and Yeovil, whilst the other larger towns rate as 'C' risk. The county is a popular holiday area and during the season the population increases considerably.

During dry weather there is a serious fire threat on the extensive heathlands of Exmoor, the Quantock Hills and the Mendip Hills.

High risk areas in the county include the Royal Ordnance Factory, Bridgwater, the nuclear power station at Hinkley Point (Nether Stowey), military establishments including the Naval Air Station at Yeovilton and Westlands Helicopters at Yeovil. The M5 Motorway crosses the county.

Wholetime recruits are trained at the Devon Fire Brigade Training School whilst retained recruits receive basis instruction at divisional level where there are also BA, HGV and other courses.

During the 1950s, the Brigade operated a number of Commers and Bedfords with HCB bodies; these were followed by Dennis F28s and then Bedford TJs and TKs bodied by HCB-Angus. Some of the early TKs remain including four with Rolls-Royce engines but 16 Bedfords and a few Dennis F28s were transferred to Avon in 1974.

During the 1970s, Dodges were purchased with Carmichael, CFE or HCB-Angus bodywork and then in 1980/81, Somerset reverted to the Bedford/HCB-Angus combination. The latest pumping appliances have been Bedfords with Saxon bodies.

Somerset operates two ERF/HCB-Angus/Simon SS50 PHPs and one ERF/CFE/Simon SS70 HP which was formerly at Blackpool and then Preston with the Lancashire Fire Brigade.

Local body builders Wincanton Motors have supplied 2 WrCs, 1 HFoT and a BAT on Bedford chassis. Ford Transits are used for two CUs and two AccUs and a new AccU is due for delivery in 1984; this is a Reynolds-Boughton 44/Rover 3500 with Saxon body (A700 RYA).

All but two stations have Land Rover 88s as L4Vs; the exceptions are Dulverton which as a Range Rover 6X4/Carmichael L4P for use on Exmoor and Burnham-on-Sea which has a Land Rover 109 as a cliff rescue unit.

WILTSHIRE
1/1 Swindon
1/2 Cricklade
1/3 Ramsbury
1/4 Stratton
1/5 Marlborough
1/6 Wootton Bassett
2/1 Chippenham
2/2 Corsham
2/3 Malmesbury
2/4 Calne
3/1 Salisbury
3/2 Wilton
3/3 Tisbury
3/4 Mere
3/5 Amesbury
3/6 Ludgershall
3/7 Pewsey
4/1 Trowbridge
4/2 Bradford-on-Avon
4/3 Melksham
4/4 Westbury
4/5 Warminster
4/6 Devizes

GLOUCESTERSHIRE
01 Lyndey
02 Coleford
03 Cinderford
04 Newent
05 Gloucester
06 Painswick
07 Stroud
08 Nailsworth
09 Wotton-under-Edge
10 Dursley
12 Cheltenham
14 Tewkesbury
15 Winchcombe
16 Chipping Campden
17 Moreton-in-Marsh
18 Stow-on-the-Wold
19 Northleach
20 Fairford
21 Cirencester
22 Tetbury

SOMERSET
01 Taunton
02 Bridgwater
03 Dulverton
04 Burnham-on-Sea
05 Cheddar
06 Porlock
07 Wellington
08 Wiveliscombe
09 Williton
10 Nether Stowey
11 Minehead
21 Yeovil
22 Crewkerne
23 Martock
24 Somerton
25 Street
26 Glastonbury
27 Wells
28 Shepton Mallet
29 Castle Cary
31 Wincanton
32 Frome
33 Ilminster
33 Chard

AVON
A1 Temple
A2 Southmead
A3 Avonmouth
A5 Patchway
A6 Thornbury
A7 Yate
B1 Bath
B2 Radstock
B3 Paulton
B4 Brislington
B5 Keynsham
B6 Speedwell
B7 Kingswood
C1 Weston-Super-Mare
C2 Clevedon
C3 Portishead
C4 Pill
C5 Bedminster
C6 Chew Magna
C7 Blagdon
C8 Winscombe
C9 Nailsea
C10 Yatton

HEREFORD & WORCESTER
28 Evesham
29 Pebworth
30 Broadway
31 Pershore
32 Upton-on-Severn
41 Malvern
42 Ledbury
43 Fownhope
44 Ross-on-Wye
45 Whitchurch

GWENT
37 Monmouth
39 Caldicot
40 Chepstow

WARWICKSHIRE
34 Shipston-on-Stour

OXFORDSHIRE
A3 Chipping Norton
A11 Burford
A12 Bampton
B3 Farringdon

ROYAL BERKSHIRE
05 Hungerford
06 Lambourn

HAMPSHIRE
C31 Andover
C33 Romsey
C34 Stockbridge
D46 Totton
D47 Fordingbridge
D48 Lyndhurst

DORSET
A4 Beaminster
A5 Maiden Newton
A9 Sherborne
A10 Sturminster Newton
A11 Gillingham
A12 Shaftesbury
A13 Blandford Forum
B20 Cranborne

DEVON
11 Lynton
14 South Molton
34 Axminster
35 Bampton
39 Cullompton
40 Honiton
44 Tiverton
46 Witheridge

FSC Fire Service College

Gwent

River Severn

37

40

39

C3

C2 C9

C10

C1

C8

C7

05

04

11 06 11 09 10 02

West

14 03 08 HQ 01 WS

35

07

46 44

Devon

39

40

33

34

SOMERSET

26 25

24

23

32 22

A4

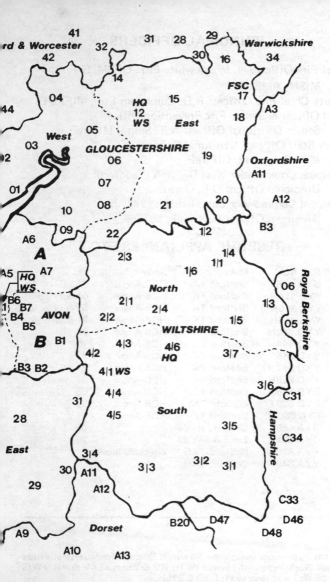

PRINCIPAL OFFICERS

Chief Fire Officer: N. Musslewhite Esq., QFSM, GIFire, MISM, AMBIM.

Deputy Chief Fire Officer: R.D. Cummings Esq., MIFire E.

Third Officer & Senior Fire Prevention Officer:
Senior Divisional Officer: N.T. Smith, MIFireE.

Senior Staff Officer: Divisional Officer
M.T. Goodman, GIFireE.

Divisional Commander West Division (Taunton):
Divisional Officer G.E. Owen.

Divisional Commander East Division (Yeovil):
Divisional Officer R. Killick, MIFireE.

RESERVE APPLIANCES ETC

Type	Reg. No.	Make	Body	ex.
WrT	UYD 175G	Bedford TJ	HCB-Angus	21
WrL	YYC 314H	Bedford TK	HCB-Angus	01 & 11 (sold)
WrT	YYC 315H	Bedford TK	HCB-Angus	02 & 11 (sold)
WrT	YYC 316H	Bedford TK	HCB-Angus	21 & 29 (sold)
WrT	YYD 842H	Bedford TK	HCB-Angus	28
WrT	YYD 844H	Bedford TK	HCB-Angus	10
WrT	YYD 846H	Bedford TK	HCB-Angus	23
WrT	YYD 847H	Bedford TK	HCB-Angus	31
WrT	YYD 848H	Bedford TK	HCB-Angus	01
WrL	DYD 628J	Bedford TK	HCB-Angus	05
WrT	DYD 629J	Bedford TK	HCB-Angus	02
WrL	FYC 689K	Bedford TK	HCB-Angus	31
L4V	OYA 659F	Land Rover 88		09
L4V	OYA 661F	Land Rover 88		26
RV	YYA 838X	Bedford TKG	Wreckers Int.	
GPL	YYA 840X	Bedford TKG		

Pictures on previous pages show Somerset Brigade Headquarters outside Brigade Workshops with reserve WrTs, RV & reserve L4V & inside W/S with 26 WrT and reserve WrT YYC 316H.

Lisieux Way, Taunton.   Risk: B, C, D.
Est: 67 — 57 W/T (1 Stn.,O., 4 Sub.O., 8 Lfm., 44 Fm.)
        10 R/T (1 Sub.O., 2 Lfm., 7 Fm.)

O.i/c: To be appointed   Av. call: 750.   Pop:58,000

110 sq. m. large market town and administrative centre with enclosed shopping precinct, industrial estates and residential area. Musgrove Park (gen.), Tone Vale & Sandhill Park (mental) Hospitals. Military establishments. Neighbouring villages in surrounding rural area with farming; Neroche Forest. M5 Motorway.

WrL	A618 0YA	Bedford TKG (d)	Saxon
WrT	KYC 873V	Bedford TKG (d)	HCB-Angus
PHP	OYB 999L	ERF 84PFS/Perkins	HCB-Angus/Simon 50'
AccU	XYC 605M	Ford Transit	
HFoT	YYA 833X	Bedford TKG (d)	Wincanton Mtrs
BAT	MYC 567P	Bedford TK	Wincanton Mtrs
L4V	JYD 248N	Land Rover	

Military FB at Norton Manor Army est.

Preserved Somerset FB Leyland Cub PE BYC 145 at 01.

Station picture incls. WrT RYD 966R (Dodge/Carmichael) now at 05.

PHOTOGRAPHS

Except where otherwise stated, all photographs in this book were taken by Simon N. Rowley and copies are available (size 8" x 6") at £1.15 each including postage from Forest Studio, Burley, Ringwood, Hants BH24 4AB.

Salmon Parade, Bridgwater.   Risk: B, C, D.

Est: 53 — 33 W/T (1 Stn.O., 4 Sub.O., 4 Lfm., 24 Fm.)
        20 R/T (1 Sub.O., 2 Lfm., 17 Fm.)

O.i/c: Stn.O. Glenton.   Av. call: 500.   Pop: 49,500

100 sq. m. large town and small inland port on River Parrett. High
risk premises incl. Royal Ordnance Factory, Puriton and B.P. petroleum
terminal, Dunball. Light industry including cellophane factory.
Surrounding villages in rural area with farming. Bridgwater (gen.),
Blake (ger.) & Marys Stanley (mat.) Hospitals. M5 Motorway.

WrL	A619 0YA	Bedford TKG (d)	Saxon
WrT	KYC 874V	Bedford TKG (d)	HCB-Angus
WrT	FYC 690K	Bedford TK	HCB-Angus
HP	PCK 999K	ERF 84PFS/Perkins	CFE/Simon 70'
		(ex. Lancs. FB/Preston CB)	
CU	KYA 428N	Ford Transit	Somerset FB
WrC	WYD 470M	Bedford KM (d)	Wincanton Mtrs.
L4V	SYA 885R	Land Rover	

MOD FB at ROF, Puriton with two Ford Transit/Bridge Coachworks
L2Ps and two Land Rovers and works FB at British Cellophane,
Bridgwater with ex. Coventry EP (NYV 40) pictured below. Now
replaced by ex. Somerset FB (11) WrT YYC 314H (Bedford TK/
HCB-Angus).

St. Cuthberts Way, Dulverton.   Risk: D

Est: 14 — (1 Stn.O., 1 Sub.O., 1 Lfm., 11 Fm.)

O.i/c: Stn.O. Snell.   Av. call: 70.   Pop: 5,500

100 sq. m. small town on edge of Exmoor with light industry. Neighbouring villages with forestry plantation, heathland and farmland in large rural area. Covering o.t.b. into Devon.

WrL	PYC 762P	Dodge K1113/Perkins	Carmichael
L4P	SYC 124L	Range Rover 6X4	Carmichael Commando
L2V	OYA 301V	Austin mini-van	

Marine Drive, Burnham-on-Sea.   Risk: D

Est: 22 — (1 Stn.O., 1 Sub.O., 3 Lfm., 17 Fm.)

O.i/c: Stn.O. Wynn.   Av. call: 230.   Pop: 24,000

60 sq. m. North Somerset seaside resort and neighbouring villages in generally flat moorland area. Holiday camps double population in summer months; large number of old people's homes. Light industry, M5 Motorway.

WrL	PYC 321L	Bedford TK/ Rolls Royce	HCB-Angus
WrT	KYC 871V	Bedford TKG/Perkins	HCB-Angus
L4V	UYD 589M	Land Rover 109	Somerset FB
(Cliff Rescue Unit)			

The Hayes, Cheddar.   Risk: D

Est: 20 — (1 Stn.O., 1 Sub.O., 2 Lfm., 16 Fm.)

O.i/c: Stn.O. Reed.   Av. call: 125.   Pop: 11,000

70 sq. m. large North Somerset village and neighbouring villages, South of Mendip Hills. Light industry and quarrying. Farmland, open heathland and forestry plantation. L.P.G. storage depot. Cliff View (mat.), St. Johns (ger.) & Shute-Shelve (ger.) hospitals.

WrL	RYD 966R	Dodge K1113/Perkins Carmichael (ex. 01)
WrT	PYC 764P	Dodge K1113/Perkins Carmichael (ex. 02)
L4V	DYA 683J	Land Rover

Station picture incls. WrL DYD 628J (Bedford/HCB-Angus) now reserve & WrT PYC 321L (Bedford/HCB-Angus) now at 11 as WrL.

Off High Street, Porlock.　　　　　　　　Risk: D

Est: 10 — (1 Sub.O., 2 Lfm., 7 Fm.)

O.i/c:　Stn.O. Floyd.　　　　　Av. call: 50　　　　　Pop: 4,000

50 sq. m. medium sized North West Somerset Village and neighbouring villages north of Exmoor; extensively rural with farming, open moorland and forestry plantation. Many thatched properties. Covering o.t.b. into Devon.

WrT　　　CYB 12S　　Dodge K1113/Perkins　CFE
L4V　　　KYA 387H　　Land Rover

Picture below shows ex. Somerset FB (06) 1961 Dennis F28 Rolls Royce WrT preserved by P. Hayes of Minehead. Driven by Barrie Martin & Steve Sully, it is pictured at the FSNBF rally, Blandford (17/7/83).

North Street, Wellington.   Risk: D

Est: 13 (1Stn.O., 2 Lfm., 10 Fm.)

O.i/c: Stn.O. Hockey.   Av. call: 180.   Pop: 15,000

80 sq. m. medium sized South West Somerset town and surrounding villages. Light industry incl. foam rubber, textiles & butane gas storage. Large rural area with agriculture. M5 Motorway, Covering o.t.b. into Devon.

WrL	FYC 92Y	Bedford TKG (d)	Saxon
L4V	XYA 389H	Land Rover	

Picture below shows former 07 WrT AYD 701B (Bedford TK/HCB-Angus) now at Chilton Cantelo School (21).

North Street, Wiveliscombe.   Risk: D

Est: 13 (1 Stn.O., 2 Lfm., 10 Fm.)

O.i/c: Stn.O. Sandford.   Av. call: 80.   Pop: 5,000

80 sq. m. small South West Somerset town and several villages in surrounding rural area. Light industry & fertilizer depot, numerous farms.

WrT	WYD 985S	Dodge K1113/Perkins HCB-Angus
L4V	PYC 333L	Land Rover

Picture below shows 01 PHP

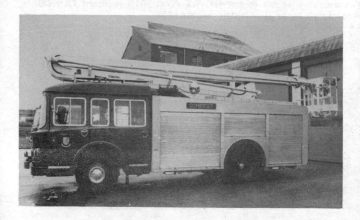

Killick Way, Williton.   Risk: C & D
Est: 20 — (1 Stn.O., 1 Sub.O., 2 Lfm., 16 Fm.)

O.i/c: Stn.O. Howells.   Av. call: 120.   Pop: 12,000

50 sq. m. small North West Somerset town and small port of Watchet;
rural area with numerous villages; heath and moorland West of
Quantock Hill. Light industry incl. paper mill complex, plastics &
wood products. Large farms and 3 hospitals (ger. & ment. hand.).

WrL	PYC 761P	Dodge K1113/Perkins Carmichael
WrT	PYC 760P	Dodge K1113/Perkins Carmichael
L4V	YYA 837X	Land Rover

Picture below shows 02 HP.

Banneson Road, Nether Stowey.   Risk: D

Est: 14 — (1 Stn.O., 2 Lfm., 11 Fm.)

O.i/c: Stn.O. Rich.   Av. call:80.   Pop:6,500

60 sq. m. medium sized North Somerset village & surrounding villages in large rural area. Extensive heathland & forestry plantation on Quantock Hills. Light industry & farming. Hinkley Point Power Station.

WrL	FYC 91Y	Bedford TKG (d)	Saxon
L4V	SYA 886R	Land Rover (with water envelope & pump for heath fires).	

Works FB at Hinkley Point Power Station (below) with WrT 22 FYD ex. Somerset FB (27) & FoT 353 MYA ex. Somerset FB (26). Both Dennis F28 Rolls Royce.

Station picture incls. former 10 WrL YYD 844H now Training App.

Hopcott Road, Minehead.   Risk: C & D

Est: 20 (1 Stn.O., 1 Sub.O., 2 Lm., 16 Fm.)

o.i/c: Stn.O. Jefferd.   Av. call: 150.   Pop: 15,000

100 sq. m. medium sized North West Somerset seaside resort (population trebles in summer). Large rural area with numerous villages. Light industry incl. chemicals & farming. Holiday camp & gen. hospital. Extensive forestry plantation & heathland on Exmoor.

WrL	PYC 324L	Bedford TK/Rolls Royce	HCB-Angus (ex. 05)
WrT	YYA 831X	Bedford TKG (d)	HCB-Angus
L4V	GYD 930K	Land Rover	

Pres. EP (Green Goddess) at West Somerset Railway.

Picture below shows pres. 1956 Commer QX/Miles PE WYA 559 (ex. 11) owned by B. Curtis & B. Brown of Reading, at FSNBF rally, Blandford Station picture incls. former WrL YYC 314H (Bedford TK/HCB-Angus)

Reckleford, Yeovil. Risk: B, C, D.

Est: 52 — 33 W/T (1 Stn.O., 4 Sub.O., 4 Lfm., 24 Fm.)
19 R/T (1 Sub.O., 2 Lfm., 16 Fm.)

O.i/c: Stn.O. Crouchman. Av. call: 500. Pop: 50,000

60 sq. m. large South Somerset market town and surrounding villages. Light industry on 4 industrial estates, tannery & helicopter factory. Rural area with farming; multi-storey District Hospital. RN Air Station, Yeovilton. Covering o.t.b. into Dorset.

WrL	A620 OYA	Bedford TKG (d)	Saxon
WrT	YYA 830X	Bedford TKG (d)	HCB-Angus
PHP	CYC 515J	ERF 84PFS/Perkins	HCB-Angus/Simon 50'
AccU	KYC 876V	Ford Transit	HCB-Angus
CU	KYA 429N	Ford Transit	Somerset FB
WrC	LYD 288P	Bedford KM (d)	Wincanton Mtrs.
L4V	JYD 249N	Land Rover	

Works FB at Westland Helicopters & RN FB at HMS Heron, Yeovilton. Chilton Cantelo School owns ex. Somerset FB (07) WrT AYD 701B Bedford TK (HCB-Angus).

Station picture incls. WrL KYC 875V now at 31 Frome.

Pics below show new Bedford TKG/Saxon WrLs A620 OYA (21) & A619 OYA (02).

Church Street, Crewkerne.   Risk: D

Est: 12 (1 Stn.O., 2 Lfm., 8 Fm.)

O.i/c: Stn.O. Frost.   Av. call: 70.   Pop: 10,000

40 sq. m. small South Somerset town and surrounding villages in rural area. Light industry and agriculture. Covering o.t.b. into Dorset.

WrL	TYC 577M	Bedford TK/ HCB-Angus (ex. 21)
		Rolls Royce
L4V	PYC 331L	Land Rover

Station picture incls. reserve WrL YYD 848H.

Picture below shows works & airfield FB at Westlands Helicopters, Yeovil; l-r are: Land Rover 88 L4V (YYB 124H), Bedford Amb. (UFX 844L), Land Rover 109 Amb. (KCR 569P), Range Rover/ Carmichael RIV (WWP 880R), Range Rover/Carmichael RIV (KYA 84N), Bedford/Foamite CrT (YYA 711), Land Rover/Carmichael L4V (7 SYA - ex. RT).

Manor Road, East Street, Martock.   Risk: D

Est: 20 (1 Stn.O., 1 Sub.O., 2 Lfm., 16 Fm.)

O.i/c: Stn.O. Gould.   Av. call: 140.   Pop: 11,000

50 sq. m. small South Somerset town and surrounding villages in rural area. Light industry and agriculture. Hospital & several elderly persons homes.

WrL	TYC 578M	Bedford TK/ Rolls Royce	HCB-Angus (ex. 07)
WrT	VYB 73W	Bedford TKG (d)	HCB-Angus
L4V	XYA 388H	Land Rover	

Preserved manual pump at Somerset FB HQ.

Picture below shows 21 AccU.

Pound Pool, Somerton.   Risk: D

Est: 12 (1 Stn.O., 2 Lfm., 9 Fm.)

O.i/c: Stn.O. Holland.   Av. call: 125.   Pop: 14,000

50 sq. m. small town South of Polden Hills with surrounding villages in rural areas. Agriculture and light industry; residential schools & homes for elderly. Forestry plantation & moorland.

| WrL | VYB 71W | Bedford TKG (d) | HCB-Angus |
| L4V | GYD 929K | Land Rover | |

Ex. Somerset FB (24) WrT RYC 470F Bedford TJ/HCB-Angus pres. by K.N. Cook of Somerton.

Picture below shows 01 H/FoT.

Cranhill Road, Street.   Risk: C & D
Est: 12 (1 Stn.O., 2 Lfm., 9 Fm.)
O.i/c: Stn.O. Eden.   Av. call: 125.   Pop: 11,000
40 sq. m. small mid Somerset town with industrial & commercial risks.
Villages in surrounding rural area with farming. Light industry includes
shoe manufacturers. Millfield Public School.

| Wrt | PYB 787P | Dodge K1113/Perkins Carmichael |
| L4V | PYC 332L | Land Rover |

Picture below shows works FB at R.O.F. Bridgwater, Puriton.

George Street, Glastonbury.　　　　　　Risk: C & D

Est: 20 (1 Stn.O., 1 Sub.O., 2 Lfm., 16 Fm.)

O.i/c:　Stn.O. Lawford.　　　　Av. Call: 150.　　　　Pop: 10,000

40 sq. m. mid Somerset market town and surrounding villages. Light industry includes sheepskin product manufacturers, large tannery with Benzine plant, and fertilizer manufacturers; agriculture.

WrL	WYD 984S	Dodge K1113/Perkins	HCB-Angus
WrT	WYD 983S	Dodge K1113/Perkins	HCB-Angus
L4V	YYA 836X	Land Rover	

Works FB (picture below) with ex. Wiltshire FB (2/2) WrT BHR 368B Bedford TK/HCB-Angus at Fisons, Ashcott Road, Meare.

Station picture incls. spare WrL YYC 315H.

Princes Road, Wells. Risk: C & D

Est: 20 (1 Stn.O., 1 Sub.O., 2 Lfm., 16 Fm.)

O.i/c: Stn.O. Morris. Av. call: 225. Pop: 15,000

50 sq. m. small city and 12 surrounding villages south of Mendip Hills. Light industry and rural area with farming and forestry plantations. Three hospitals boarding schools & Wells Cathedral.

WrL	CYB 13S	Dodge K1113/Perkins	CFE
WrT	CYB 14S	Dodge K1113/Perkins	CFE
L4V	DYA 682J	Land Rover	

Station picture incls. Reserve L4V OYA 659F (ex. 09).

Picture below shows Somerset FB pres. Leyland Cub PE BYC 145 at 01.

Board Cross, Shepton Mallet.   Risk: C & D

Est: 20 (1 Stn.O., 1 Sub.O., 2 Lfm., 16 Fm.)

O.i/c: Stn.O. White   Av. call: 220.   Pop: 16,000

60 sq. m. small East Somerset town and neighbouring villages. Light industry incl. chemicals & soft drink manufacturers. Rural area with farming & forestry plantation. Two hospitals & boarding schools.

WrL	DYD 627J	Bedford TK	HCB-Angus
WrT	YYA 832X	Bedford TKG (d)	HCB-Angus
L4V	VYC 207M	Land Rover	

Picture below shows 01 BAT.

Millbrook Gardens, Castle Cary.   Risk: D

Est: 12 (1 Stn.O., 2 Lfm., 9 Fm.)

O.i/c: Stn.O. Marsh.   Av. call: 100.   Pop: 9,000

60 sq. m. small South East Somerset town and surrounding villages. Light industry and several large boarding schools. Rural area with agriculture.

WrT	FYC 93Y	Bedford TKG (d)	Saxon
L4V	SYA 787R	Land Rover	

Station picture incls. former WrT YYC 316H (Bedford TK/HCB-Angus).

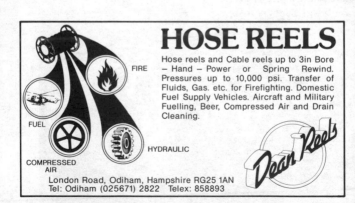

South Street, Wincanton.   Risk: D

Est: 12 (1 Stn.O., 2 Lfm., 9 Fm.)

O.i/c: Stn.O. Broughton.   Av. call: 100.   Pop: 8,500

40 sq. m. small South East Somerset town and surrounding villages. Rural area with farming and light industry. Two hospitals & boarding schools.

WrL	VYB 72W	Bedford TKG (d)	HCB-Angus (ex. 01)
L4V	OYA 660F	Land Rover	

Firemen at Stn. 30 maintain ex. Somerset FB (30) WrT UYD 179G Bedford TJ/HCB-Angus.

Picture below shows 21 WrC.

Keyford, Frome.   Risk: C & D

Est: 20 (1 Stn.O., 1 Sub.O., 2 Lfm., 16 Fm.)

O.i/c: Stn.O. Cox   Av. call: 300.   Pop: 30,000

70 sq. m. medium sized North East Somerset town and 18 surrounding villages. Light industry of varying risks and agriculture in rural area. 7 large quarry installations, 3 hospitals; forestry plantation.

WrL	KYC 875V	Bedford TKG (d)	HCB-Angus
WrT	KYC 872V	Bedford TKG (d)	HCB-Angus (ex. 21)
L4V	GYD 931K	Land Rover	

Station picture incls. former 31 WrL FYC 689K now reserve.

Picture below shows RV at Workshops.

Butts Road, Ilminster.   Risk: C & D

Est: 12 (1 Stn.O., 2 Lfm., 9 Fm.)

O.i/c: Stn.O. Coles.   Av. call: 110.   Pop: 9,500

45 sq.m. South Somerset market town and surrounding villages. Medium engineering and light industry; rural area with farming. Royal Naval Air Station, Dillington House College.

WrT	PYC 763P	Dodge K1113/Perkins Carmichael
L4V	UYD 587M	Land Rover

Picture below shows 21 CU.

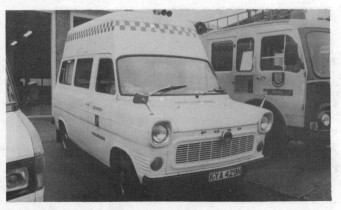

Tapstone Road, Chard.   Risk: C & D

Est: 14 (1 Stn.O., 2 Lfm., 11 Fm.)

O.i/c: Stn.O. Farley.   Av. call: 135.   Pop: 14,500

50 sq. m. small South Somerset town and neighbouring villages. Varied light industry and agriculture in rural area. Chard Geriatric Hospital; forestry plantation. Covering o.t.b. into Devon and Dorset.

WrL	PYC 323L	Bedford TK/ Rolls Royce	HCB-Angus (ex. 01)
L4V	PYC 330L	Land Rover	

Picture below shows 21 PHP.

RETAINED FIREFIGHTERS UNION

Here are some of the reasons why you should join the RFU whose policy is to "Uphold, maintain and further the long established tradition of Retained & Volunteer Firefighters serving the Community *efficiently, economically,* and *selflessly.*"

★ We have been recognised by many Brigades in the United Kingdom.
★ We have a Personal Accident Scheme paying £50 a week for two years, £5,000 on death to next of kin — for a fiver a year in G.B.
★ We have a Mutual Aid Fund, currently paying £100 in cash immediately to next of kin.
★ We have NO STRIKE and NO CLOSED SHOP Rules.
★ We have a free Legal Aid Scheme, which entitles a Member to representation by a solicitor or Counsel, from your home town.
★ We have TOTAL COMMITMENT to Retained and Volunteer Firefighters.
★ We have united Accountants, Coalminers, Engineers, Foremen, Mechanics, Safety Officers, officials of many Unions, Workers of most Trades, Professions and the Self-Employed into a unique Union.
★ This collective knowledge cannot be matched by any other union, and is available to all Members as Firefighters or for their primary jobs.
★ We advise Members with problems about redundancy, employment contracts, tax, banking, social security, workplace accidents, discipline etc.
★ We are the only F.S. union with a massive 86% support proven by A.C.A.S. in its National Ballot.
★ We are the only organization entirely dovoted to the Retained Service and to the unique brotherhood of Retained and Volunteer Firefighters.

THE RFU REALLY REPRESENTS RETAINED!

We know your needs and have earned your support.

NOW JOIN US!

The RFU is respected not by the argument of force but by the force of argument. Our legal arguments have won for Retained Firefighters — the right to a Contract of Employment; the right to Redundancy Payments; to appeal against dismissal to an Industrial Tribunal; to exclude F.S. earnings for Unemployment Benefit; to represent Retained by Retained; to consult and be consulted; to hold meetings on Stations, to use Station notice-boards and to have subs. deducted at source. Best of all, the Retained Firefighters Union have won their High-Court action in December 1983, for the right of retained members to participate in the Local Government Superannuation Scheme.

At a time when Brigades demand more and more from RETAINED FIRE-FIGHTERS; at a time when the risks get bigger and the rewards comparatively less — RETAINED and VOLUNTEER FIREFIGHTERS CANNOT RISK NOT JOINING THE RETAINED FIRE-FIGHTERS UNION.

Send a note for more details to:

**The General Secretary,
Retained Firefighters Union,
FirefighterHouse, Woodville Road,
Maidstone, Kent ME15 7BS. Tel: 0622 62455.**

or leave your name and address
on our 24 hour answering tape
and receive full details by
return post.

COUNTY OF AVON

FIRE BRIGADE

The County of Avon Fire Brigade was formed on April 1st 1974 when the new County of Avon was created by the Local Government Reorganization.

The County Brigade took control of the six stations of the City and County of Bristol Fire Brigade, the City of Bath Fire Brigade's one station, four stations from the Gloucestershire Fire Service and 14 stations from the Somerset Fire Brigade.

Since then a former Gloucestershire D/M station at A4 Severnside (Pilning) was closed as were former Somerset volunteer stations at Banwell and Wrington.

There are now 23 stations of which 10 are W/T, one D/M and 12 R/T.

Avon lies on the south eastern side of the Mouth of the River Severn. Bristol is the major centre of population and industry with a dockland area at Avonmouth, whilst the historic City of Bath and the resort of Weston-Super-Mare are popular tourist areas.

Notable risks include the varied dockland industries, Oldbury power station and the M4, M5 and M32 Motorways, including the Severn Road Bridge which has a dual attendance with Gwent. Avon also has a considerable rural area.

The county is divided into three divisions, 'A' Division (6 stations) covers central Bristol and the north Avon area with Div. HQ at Temple Back; 'B' Division (7 stations) covers the east and south east with Div. HQ at Bath whilst 'C' Division (10 stations) covers the south and south west with Weston-Super-Mare as Div. HQ.

Brigade HQ is in a purpose built complex which houses the fire station at Temple Back, Bristol. Also in the complex are brigade workshops and training school. There are also workshops at Divisonal HQs.

Fire control is at HQ and deals with about 12,000 calls annually. The control room is at present being refurbished and should be completed by May. Stations are turned out using the "Solent" system backed up by computer for PDAs. Retained personnel are summoned by pocket alerters.

Recruits both wholetime and retained are trained at the Brigade Training School which also provides continuation courses including junior basic command, breathing apparatus and HGV driving.

The Fire Prevention Department is based at HQ with offices at divisional level and is responsible for the statutory inspections and issue of fire certificates, whilst goodwill advice and lectures on fire safety are given regularly to the general public.

When the Brigade was formed it inherited a variety of pumping and special appliances. A large number of the pumps have now been sold with the exception of ex. Somerset Bedford/HCB-Angus WrTs, five ex Bristol ERF/HCB-Angus WrTs (formerly WrEs) and a Dodge/ERF WrE at Training School.

The fleet has been standardised using Dodge appliances with Perkins diesel engines and HCB-Angus bodywork. In 1983 four Dodge/Merryweather WrLs were purchased.

Avon has four TLs (two each AEC/Merryweather & Dodge/Carmichael/Magirus), a Major RT (Dodge/Wreckers International), three RTs (one each Dodge/HCB-Angus, Dodge/Carmichael, Land Rover/Carmichael, two HPs (one each Dodge/HCB-Angus/Simon 26m & Dodge/Evans/Simon 22m), two FoTs (one each Dodge/Carmichael & Ford/HCB-Angus), a BAT/CU and a HL (both Bedford/Oldland), a ST/CIU (Bedford/Taylors) and two HRTs (Land Rover/HCB-Angus).

A display unit using a former Bath Dennis F108 WrT attends shows and functions promoting fire prevention.

Pictures on this & Previous 3 pages show Avon Fire Brigade HQ, Temple Back, Bristol. Driver Training GPVs & L4Vs. Training WrE HAE 418K & WrT FYC 688K. Brigade W/S with RV & T/S WrL YYD 841H. Brigade W/S with B4 CIU & A3 TL.

PRINCIPAL OFFICERS

Chief Fire Officer: F.G. Wilton Esq., MIFireE., FBIM.
    Deputy Chief Fire Officer: P.W. Aris Esq., FIFireE.
Assistant Chief Fire Officer: D. Boyne Esq.,
Senior Staff Officer: Senior Divisional Officer
    A.J. Townsend MIFireE.
Divisional Commander 'A' Division (Temple):
    Divisional Officer M.J. Britton GIFireE.
Divisional Commander 'B' Division (Bath):
    Divisional Officer G.T. Iles MIFireE.
Divisional Commander 'C' Division (Weston-Super-Mare):
    Divisional Officer B.M. Hellin MIFireE.

RESERVE APPLIANCES ETC

Type	Reg. No.	Make	Body	Stn.	ex.
WrL	RHW 378S	Dodge K1113/Perkins	HCB-Angus	B4	B4
WrL	LWS 732P	Dodge K1113/Perkins	HCB-Angus	A2	A1
WrT	LWS 735P	Dodge K1113/Perkins	HCB-Angus	B6	B5
WrL	GTC 949N	Dodge K850/Perkins	HCB-Angus	C1	C5, C6
WrL	GTC 950N	Dodge K850/Perkins	HCB-Angus	A1	A3
WrL	HOU 646N	Dodge K850/Perkins	HCB-Angus	A3	A1, A6
WrL	TAE 680M	Dodge K850/Perkins	HCB-Angus	C5	A1
WrT	PYC 322L	Bedford TK/Rolls Royce	HCB-Angus	B2	SFB, C1
WrT	BDG 674K	Ford D1013	HCB-Angus	*	GFS, A4
WrL	BDG 942K	Ford D1013	HCB-Angus	*	GFS, A5
WrT	FYC 688K	Bedford TK	HCB-Angus	TS	SFB, C1, C7
WrL	YYD 841H	Bedford TK	HCB-Angus	TS	SFB, C8
WrT	YYD 845H	Bedford TK	HCB-Angus	C1	SFB, C10
WrT	YYD 843H	Bedford TK	HCB-Angus	*	SFB, C2
WrT	UYD 177G	Bedford TK	HCB-Angus	*	SFB, C4
WrT**	GGL 131G	Dennis F108/Perkins	Dennis	A2	B1
WrE	HAE 418K	Dodge K850/Perkins	ERF	TS	C5, B1
RT/LU	MFB 471	Land Rover	Carmichael	B3	B1
RV	UHW 952T	Land Rover 109	—	WS	—
L4V	HHU 879N	Land Rover 109	—	DS	—
L4V	JAE 999D	Land Rover 109	HCB-Angus	B1	A1 (HRT)
GPL	MTC 632R	Commer G1385/Perkins	—	DS	
GPL	LFB 899P	Commer G1385/Perkins	—	DS	

KEY: ** — Display Unit; * — sold; DS — Driving School; TS — Training School; WS — Workshops.

NB: Where O.i/c of stations are shown as A.D.Os, these are supervisory officers hence "(SO)".

A1 TEMPLE — W/T (1973)

Temple Back, Bristol.   Risk: A - C

Est: 96 — (4 Stn.O., 8 Sub.O., 12 Lfm., 72 Fm.)

O.i/c: (SO) — A.D.O. Townley. Av. call: 2,200.   Pop: 20,000

60 sq. m. Bristol City centre with shopping and commercial centres, industrial estates, several hospitals & former dock area. High rise offices & flats with multi occupancy converted houses in typical inner city area. Bristol University & Cathedral; M32 Motorway.

WrL	DHY 525W	Dodge G1313/Perkins	HCB-Angus
WrT	DHY 526W	Dodge G1313/Perkins	HCB-Angus
WrT	DHY 529W	Dodge G1313/Perkins	HCB-Angus
RT	RHW 386S	Dodge K1113/Perkins	HCB-Angus
TL	RHW 385S	Dodge G1613/Perkins	Carmichael/Magirus
BAT/CU	EHW 746K	Bedford TK	Oldland Bodies

Station picture incls. demo-unit (former WrT) GGL 131G Dennis F108 (ex. B1) now at A2.

A2 SOUTHMEAD — W/T (1960)

Southmead Road, Westbury-on-Trim, Bristol.   Risk: B & C

Est: 33 — (1 Stn.O., 4 Sub. O., 4 Lfm., 24 Fm.)

O.i/c: Stn.O. Rivers.   Av. call: 1,000   Pop: 187,000

20 sq. m. North West suburbs of Bristol with high rise buildings, hospitals & colleges. Industrial estates with varied light industry. Ministry of Agriculture Research Establishment.

WrL	NEU 560Y	Dodge G1313/Perkins	Merryweather
HL	EHW 747K	Bedford TK	Oldland Bodies

Station picture incls. former WrT RHW 377S (Dodge/HCB-Angus) now at A6 & former FoC HAE 999D (Karrier/HCB-Angus, ex. A3) used by FSNBF but now withdrawn.

A3 AVONMOUTH — W/T (1958)

St. Andrews Road, Avonmouth, Bristol.   Risk: A — D

Est: 60 — (4 Stn.O., 4 Sub.O., 8 Lfm., 44 Fm.)

O.i/c: (SO) — A.D.O. Clark.   Av. call: 500   Pop: 40,000

20 sq. m. Western industrial area of Bristol bordering River Severn. Dockland and industrial estates with heavy & light industry incl. petro chemical & pharmaceutical. Residential suburbs & rural areas. M5 Motorway.

WrL	HAE 882X	Dodge G1313/Perkins	HCB-Angus
WrT	HAE 881X	Dodge G1313/Perkins	HCB-Angus
TL	PAE 999F	AEC Mercury	Merryweather
FoT	CAE 856J	Dodge K1050/Perkins	Carmichael
GPL	VFB 938T	Commer G08 (used as FoC).	

Works FB at ICI with L2P (Volkswagen).

Station picture incls. reserve WrT BDG 942K (Ford D1013/HCB-Angus) ex. Glos. & A5 Patchway (now withdrawn).

A5 PATCHWAY — W/T (1966)

Rodway Road, Patchway, Bristol. Risk: B, C, D.

Est: 41 — (1 Stn.O., 4 Sub.O., 4 Lfm., 32 Fm.)

O.i/c: Stn.O. Hutchings. Av. call: 1,200 Pop: 175,000

70 sq. m. Northern suburbs of Bristol and villages in large rural area bordering and east of River Severn. Considerable light industry, British Aerospace/Rolls Royce complex & airfield. Several hospitals; M5, M6 & M32 Motorways and Severn Bridge. (Formerly part of Gloucestershire FS).

| WrL | RHW 381S | Dodge K1113/Perkins | HCB-Angus |
| MRT | KTC 601P | Dodge K1613/Perkins | Wreckers Int. |

Works FB at British Aerospace, Filton with CrTs, RIVs, FoT & L2P. (Picture under B4).

A6 THORNBURY — R/T (1980)

Gloucester Road, Thornbury.   Risk: C & D

Est: 20 — (1 Stn.O., 1 Sub.O., 4 Lfm., 14 Fm.)

O.i/c: Stn.O. Foulger.   Av. call: 250.   Pop: 20,000

50 sq. m. small market town in North Avon and surrounding villages in rural area, bordering and east of River Severn. Light industry & farming. Hospital (ger.) & nuclear power station. Covering o.t.b. into Gloucestershire. (Formerly part of Gloucestershire FS).

WrT   RHW 377S   Dodge K1113/Perkins HCB-Angus (ex. A2)
WrT   UHW 950T   Dodge K1113/Perkins HCB-Angus (ex. B7)

Works FB at Oldbury Power Station with former Gloucestershire FS appliances: WrT DAD 721C (Commer VA6/Dennis) ex. 02; WrT NAD 753 (Commer/Miles) ex. 07; RT MDD 648 (Commer/Miles ex. WrT); Dennis FoTr.

A7 YATE — D/M (1969)

Station Road, Yate.   Risk: C & D
Est: 26 — 14 W/T (1 Stn.O., 1 Sub.O., 3 Lfm., 9 Fm)
          12 R/T (1 Sub.O., 2 Lfm., 9 Fm.)

O.i/c: Stn.O. Gardner.   Av. call: 420   Pop: 42,000

110 sq. m. small North East Avon towns of Yate and Chipping Sodbury with numerous villages in large rural area. Industrial estates with light industry incl. plastics & ink manufacturers. Agriculture & forestry plantation. Badminton House. M4 Motorway. (Formerly part of Gloucestershire FS).

WrT   UHW 948T   Dodge K1113/Perkins   HCB-Angus (ex. B6)
WrT   DAE 621K   ERF 84PF/Perkins   HCB-Angus (ex. A1)

Picture below shows A1 RT.

B1 BATH — W/T (1939)

Cleveland Bridge, Bathwick Street, Bath.   Risk: B, C, D.

Est: 80 — 68 W/T (4 Stn.O., 4 Sub.O., 8 Lfm., 52 Fm.)
            12 R/T (1 Sub.O., 2 Lfm., 9 Fm.)

O.i/c: (SO) — A.D.O. Hacker.   Av. call: 1,000.   Pop: 120,000

130 sq. m. Historic Georgian City of Bath with commercial & residential areas and villages in large surrounding rural area. Heavy & light industry; numerous hospitals, old peoples' homes, hotels & boarding schools. High pressure gas reducing station, Bath Abbey, Covering o.t.b. into Wiltshire.

WrL	DHY 523W	Dodge G1313/Perkins	HCB-Angus
WrT	DHY 524W	Dodge G1313/Perkins	HCB-Angus
WrT	KTC 605P	Dodge K1113/Perkins	HCB-Angus
RT	NGL 999L	Land Rover 109	Carmichael
TL	EGL 678F	AEC Mercury	Merryweather

Works FB at Stothert & Pitt, Bath with Bedford BAT & L4P.

B2 RADSTOCK — R/T (1960)

Wells Road, Radstock.   Risk: C & D

Est: 12 — (1 Stn.O., 2 Lfm., 9 Fm.)

O.i/c: Stn.O. Coles.   Av. call: 210.   Pop: 22,000

40 sq. m. small South Avon town in developing urban area with surrounding villages. Industrial estates with light industry incl. printing factory. Rural area with agriculture. Covering o.t.b. into Somerset. (Formerly part of Somerset FB).

WrL   UHW 951T   Dodge K1113/Perkins   HCB-Angus

Station picture incls. reserve WrT BDG 674K (Ford D1013/HCB-Angus) ex. Glos & A4 Severnside (now withdrawn).

Picture below shows B1 RT.

Park Corner, Paulton.　　　　　　　Risk: C & D

Est: 12 — (1 Stn.O., 2 Lfm., 9 Fm.)

O.i/c:　Stn.O. Bevan.　　　　Av. call: 180.　　　　Pop: 15,000

25 sq. m. small South Avon town and nine neighbouring villages in rural area. Light industry, incl. printing factory and farming. Cottage hospital & Cheshire Home. Covering o.t.b. into Somerset. (Formerly part of Somerset FB).

WrT　　　　UHW 947T　　Dodge K1113/Perkins　HCB-Angus

Picture below shows reserve RT/LU MFB 471 (Land Rover/Carmichael) and former HRT JAE 999D (Land Rover/HCB-Angus) at B1.

B4 BRISLINGTON — W/T (1962)

Bonville Road, Brislington, Bristol. Risk: B, C, D.

Est: 33 — (1 Stn.O., 4 Sub.O., 4 Lfm., 24 Fm.)

O.i/c: Stn.O. Jackson. Av. call: 660. Pop: 80,000

10 sq. m. South West suburbs of Bristol. Residential with some rural cover & several large industrial estates with varied light industry. incl. paint manufacturers, BR HST servicing depot, CEGB main control, hospitals.

WrL	NEU 560Y	Dodge G1313/Perkins	Merryweather
ST/CIU	BHW 486J	Bedford TK	Taylors (ex. B6) (former Decon U)

Picture below shows works and airfield FB at British Aerospace, Filton (A5 ground).

Temple Street, Keynsham.   Risk: C & D

Est: 12 – (1 Stn.O., 2 Lfm., 9 Fm.)

O.i/c: Stn.O. Clarke.   Av. call: 170.   Pop: 32,250

0 sq. m. medium sized market town, South West of Bristol with several neighbouring villages. Industrial estates with light industry incl. paper mills, chocolate factory & paint storage. Geriatric hospital, MOD establishment. (Formerly part of Somerset FB).

WrT   GTC 948N   Dodge K850/Perkins   HCB-Angus

Station picture incls. reserve WrL LWS 735P (Dodge K1113 HCB-Angus) ex. B6 & B5, & preserved Dennis F28 (1961) 703 LYA ex. Somerset & B3 Paulton (used by FSNBF), pictured below.

res. ex Lulsgate Airport FoT (Austin K6/Pyrene) at Trout Inn, Temple St., Keynsham.

B6 SPEEDWELL — W/T (1952)

Speedwell Road, Speedwell, Bristol.　　　Risk: B & C

Est: 60 — (4 Stn.O., 4 Sub.O., 4 Lfm., 48 Fm.)

O.i/c:　T/B/A.　　　　　Av. call: 1,000.　　　Pop: 60,000

12 sq. m. North East suburbs of Bristol, mainly residential with high rise buildings, but with light industry on industrial estates, several hospitals and homes for aged. M32 Motorway.

WrL	HAE 879X	Dodge G1313/Perkins	HCB-Angus
WrT	HAE 880X	Dodge G1313/Perkins	HCB-Angus
HP	DHY 531W	Dodge G1613/Perkins	Evans/Simon (22m)

(supplied by Carmichael)

Tenniscourt Road, Kingswood, Bristol.   Risk: B, C, D.

Est: 33 — (1 Stn.O., 4 Sub.O., 4 Lfm., 23 Fm.)

O.i/c: Stn.O., Lawes.   Av. call: 700.   Pop: 100,000

50 sq. m. Eastern suburbs of Bristol and neighbouring villages in large rural area. Residential with light industry on industrial estates. Gas distribution depot, hospitals & agriculture. (Formerly part of Gloucester-shire FS).

| WrL | NEU 561Y | Dodge G1313/Perkins | Merryweather |
| FoT | KDF 832E | Ford D600 | HCB-Angus (ex. A4 & A3) |

C1 WESTON-SUPER-MARE — W/T (1960)

Milton Avenue, Weston-Super-Mare.   Risk: B, C, D.

Est: 80 — 68 W/T (4 Stn.O., 4 Sub.O., 8 Lfm., 52 Fm.)
12 R/T (1 Sub.O., 2 Lfm., 9 Fm.)

O.i/c: (SO) — A.D.O. Underhay. Av. call: 600.   Pop: 60,000

40 sq. m. large seaside resort in South West Avon on Bristol Channel.
Numerous hotels & holiday camps (population quadruples in holiday
season). Villages in rural area with farming. Light industry incl.
helicopter const. with airfield; hospitals, M5 Motorway. Covering o.t.b.
into Somerset. (Formerly part of Somerset FB).

WrL	NEU 563Y	Dodge G1313/Perkins	Merryweather
WrT	DHY 528W	Dodge G1313/Perkins	HCB-Angus
WrT	BHT 448J	ERF 84PF/Perkins	HCB-Angus (ex. B4 WrE)
RT	AHU 388V	Dodge G1313/Perkins	CFE
HP	FHY 197K	Dodge K1050/Perkins	HCB-Angus/Simon (26m) (ex. A1)
HRT	UHW 482H	Land Rover 109	HCB-Angus (ex. B6)

Station picture incls. WrL RHW 380S (Dodge/HCB-Angus) now at C6
as WrT.

Works FB at Westlands Airfield. Mr. A. Guise owns ex. Glos. FB, then
Avon (A5 & C1) WrT PDF 923G (Ford D600/HCB-Angus).

C2 CLEVEDON — R/T (1921*)

Old Street, Clevedon.   Risk: C & D

Est: 20 — (1 Stn.O., 1 Sub.O., 2 Lfm., 16 Fm.)

O.i/c: Stn.O. Willcocks.   Av. call: 210.   Pop: 25,000

25 sq. m. medium sized West Avon town on Mouth of River Severn.
Neighbouring villages in rural area with farming. Light industry on
trading estates. Cottage Hospital, M5 Motorway. (Formerly part of
Somerset FB).

| WrL | RHW 379S | Dodge K1113/Perkins | HCB-Angus |
| WrT | VHU 175H | ERF 84PF/Perkins | HCB-Angus (ex. A2 WrE) |

*Station building built around 1850 as pumping station, then used as
council offices before conversion to fire station.

Kenn Garage, Clevedon has pres. ex. Wiltshire FB (1/1 Swindon) WrT
GMR 269D (Bedford/HCB-Angus).

Picture below shows C1 ET.

C3 PORTISHEAD – R/T (1952)

Station Road, Portishead. Risk: A, C, D.

Est: 20 – (1 Stn.O., 1 Sub.O., 2 Lfm., 16 Fm.)

O.i/c: Stn.O. Vowles   Av. call: 110.   Pop: 20,000

25 sq. m. medium sized West Avon town on Mouth of River Severn & neighbouring villages. Dockland area with warehouses; light industry, rural area with agriculture. (Formerly part of Somerset FB).

WrL	UHW 949T	Dodge K1113/Perkins	HCB-Angus
WrT	RHT 999G	ERF 84PF/Perkins	HCB-Angus (ex. B6 WrE)

Picture below shows A1 BAT/CU.

Westward Drive, Pill.   Risk: C & D

Est: 12 (1 Stn.O., 2 Lfm., 9 Fm.)

O.i/c: Stn.O. Shilton.   Av. call: 90.   Pop: 7,000

40 sq. m. large village & neighbouring villages West of Bristol in rural area with light industry and farming. Two hospitals, M5 Motorway. (Formerly part of Somerset FB).

WrT   LWS 734P   Dodge K1113/Perkins HCB-Angus (ex. C5)

Picture below shows reserve WrTs at C1 **UYD 177G (Bedford TJ/ HCB-Angus) ex. C4 (now sold)** and **YYD 845H (Bedford TK/HCB-Angus)** ex. C10.

C5 BEDMINSTER — W/T (1964)

Hartcliffe Way, Bedminster, Bristol.   Risk: B, C, D.

Est: 60 — (4 Stn.O., 4 Sub.O., 4 Lfm., 48 Fm.)

O.i/c: (SO) — A.D.O. Perrott.   Av. call: 1,300.   Pop: 175,000

40 sq. m. South & South West suburbs of Bristol. Mainly residential but with light industry, incl. tannery, on industrial estates. Several hospitals. Villages in rural area; Lulsgate (Bristol) Airport (commercial).

WrL	DHY 530W	Dodge G1313/Perkins	HCB-Angus
WrT	DHY 527W	Dodge G1313/Perkins	HCB-Angus
TL	RHW 384S	Dodge G1613/Perkins	Carmichael/Magirus
HRT	UHW 481S	Land Rover 109	HCB-Angus

Station picture incls. reserve WrT LWS 732P (Dodge/HCB-Angus) ex. A1.

MCA FB at Lulsgate Airport with CrT, FoT & RiVs.

Tunbridge Road, Chew Magna.   Risk: D

Est: 12 — (1 Sub.O., 2 Lfm., 9Fm.)

O.i/c: Sub.O. Parsons.   Av. call: 100.   Pop: 7,000

0 sq. m. medium sized South Avon village and surrounding villages in
ural area. Light industry and agriculture. Hospital, Chew Valley Lake
large expanse of open water). (Formerly part of Somerset FB).

WrT   RHW 380S   K1113/Perkins   HCB-Angus (ex. C1)

Station picture shows WrT GTC 949N (Dodge K850/HCB-Angus)
ormerly C5 & C6 (now reserve).

Picture below shows former city of Bath WrT GGL 131G (Dennis F108)
now used as display unit.

C7 BLAGDON — R/T (1971)

Station Road, Blagdon. Risk: D

Est: 12 — (1 Stn.O., 2 Lfm., 9 Fm.)

O.i/c: Stn.O. Skillman. Av. call: 75. Pop: 7,000

40 sq. m. medium sized South Avon village and neighbouring villages in Mendip Hills. Rural areas with farming and light industry; heathland & forestry plantation. Blagdon Lake (large expanse of open water). Covering o.t.b. into Somerset. (Formerly part of Somerset FB).

WrT LWS 736P Dodge K1113/Perkins HCB-Angus (ex. A3)

Picture below shows B7 FoT.

C8 WINSCOMBE — R/T (1953)

Sandford Road, Winscombe.   Risk: D

Est: 12 — (1 Stn.O., 2 Lfm., 9 Fm.)

O.i/c: Stn.O. Mabbett.   Av. call: 120.   Pop: 11,000

40 sq. m. large South Avon village & neighbouring villages incl. Banwell. Rural area, west of Mendip Hills with heathland and forestry plantation. Light industry & farming. Covering o.t.b. into Somerset. (Formerly part of Somerset FB).

WrT   KTC 603P   Dodge K1113/Perkins HCB-Angus (ex. A7)

Former vol. firemen at closed C9 Banwell own ex. Somerset, then Avon C1, C3 & T/S WrL FYB 471C (Bedford TJ/HCB-Angus).

Picture below shows former A3 FoC (Karrier/HCB-Angus) since used by FSNBF but now withdrawn.

C9 NAILSEA — R/T (1973)

Pound Lane, Nailsea.   Risk: C & D

Est: 20 — (1 Stn.O., 1 Sub.O., 2 Lfm., 16 Fm.)

O.i/c: Stn.O. Wyatt   Av. call: 180.   Pop: 23,000

35 sq. m. medium sized West Avon town and surrounding villages. Light industry, incl. paint manufacturer on industrial estates. Agriculture in rural area. Two hospitals. (Formerly part of Somerset FB).

WrL	LWS 733P	Dodge K1113/Perkins	HCB-Angus
WrT	VHU 174H	ERF 84PF/Perkins	HCB-Angus (ex. A3)

Station picture incls. reserve WrL TAE 680M (Dodge/HCB-Angus) ex. A1.

Picture below shows W/5 at C1 with C9 WrL LWS 733P, mobile workshop FHT 673W (Dodge S50) and Ford Escort L2V.

C10 YATTON – R/T (1974)

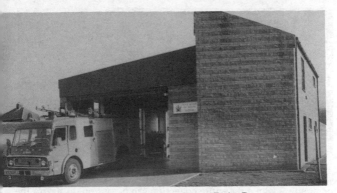

Rock Road, Yatton.   Risk: D

Est: 12 – (1 Stn.O., 2 Lfm., 9 Fm.)

O.i/c: Stn.O. Keedwell.   Av. call: 110.   Pop: 9,00(

40 sq. m. large South West Avon village & surrounding villages incl.
Wrington. Light industry & agriculture in rural areas. Yatton Hospital.
(Formerly part of Somerset FB).

WrT   KTC 602P   Dodge K1113/Perkins HCB-Angus (ex. C1)

Bell Inn, Congresbury has pres. ex. Glamorgan County FB 1955 PL
(Dennis F12/Rolls Royce) PTX 827.

**Picture below shows appliances at Lulsgate Airport (C5 ground) with
Range Rover/Carmichael RiV (YAY 193V), Thornycroft CrT (XHU
593H) and Chubb CrT (EHW 903W).**

BRISTOL FIRE MUSEUM GROUP

The Bristol Fire Museum Group have a collection of old appliances which are kept at various locations in the City. The Group is looking for premises where the entire collection can be put on display to the public. Group Secretary is Ian Morrisey (Bristol 686300).

The collection consists of:

Former City of Bath FB (1963) NGL 664 Bedford TK/HCB-Angus (pictured above).

Former Bristol City WrT (1953) RHT 553 Bedford S/HCB (ex. Bedminster) pictured under 4/1 (Wiltshire) when it was works appliance at Airsprung, Trowbridge.

Former Somerset FB Type 'A' WrT (1950) MYB 902 Commer/Whitson (ex. Paulton) — pictured below.

Former Gloucestershire FB Pump (1960) 1600 AD Bedford/Carmichael/Hawson (ex. Chipping Sodbury & Yate) — pictured below.

Former Devon FB WrL (1964) 207 PTA Bedford TJ/HCB-Angus (ex. Torquay, Painton & Brixham).

Former B.O.C.M. works FB (Avonmouth Docks) HRT (1963) 680 UHY Land Rover/Carmichael.

Former C.E.G.B. Harland TrP (1940).

Former Bristol Ambulance Service Amb. (1964) AHY 438B Morris/Appleyard.

FIRE SERVICE COLLEGE, MORETON-IN-MARSH GLOUCESTERSHIRE

A Fire Servcie College was first established in Brighton during World War II to provide training for members of the National Fire Service. When the fire service returned to local authority control in 1948 the College was retained and in 1951 moved to Wotton House near Dorking. In 1968 a Fire Service Technical College was established at Moreton-in-Marsh at which time the College near Dorking was renamed the Fire Service Staff College providing command and staff training for the senior officers in the service. In 1981 the Staff College vacated Wotton House and amalgamated with the Technical College at Moreton-in-Marsh, the newly combined establishment being re-designated the Fire Service College.

The Fire Service College provides operational, specialist, command and management training for both junior and senior ranks in the service. The site at Moreton-in-Marsh was originally an RAF airfield and was first used by the fire service in 1956 for training officers and men of the whole-time and part-time fire service, the Auxiliary Fire Service, the Territorial Army and RAF reservists in war-time fire-fighting techniques. The College buldings, which are all purpose-built, were provided for the Home Office by the Property Services Agency of the Department of the Environment which was responsible for the detailed designs. Building work was carried out in four phases starting in 1967; the opening of the sports complex in 1976 completed the fourth phase. Since then certain additional facilities have been provided, such as a new Road Traffic Accident Training block, reflecting a policy of continual up-dating to meet the training needs of the Service.

The College's facilities include: dormitory blocks for 470 students and 36 staff and provision for messing and recreational activities; general or specialised instructional class and syndicate rooms, a lecture theatre, a library and laboratories, all incorporating the latest instructional aids, including closed circuit television; and a comprehensive fireground training area, with specialised buildings in which training in all forms of fire-fighting can be given under realistic conditions of heat, smoke and fire.

The College staff is directed by the Commandant. He is supported by a Deputy Commandant, an Assistant Commandant, a civilian Director of Studies, a Secretary and a staff of fire service officers (mostly from brigades in the United Kingdom) and civilian tutors, who work closely together and provide students with the knowledge to enable them to understand the technical demands made upon them, to develop their general education to the academic level essential in the supervisory ranks in the Service, and to develop the command and management abilities of the more senior officers. The College also has a number of visiting lecturers who are specialists in their own field.

The fireground is believed to be the most advanced and comprehensive in the world and incorportates many unique features. It has a control

tower, from which the safety of the students under training is monitored by measuring and recording the temperature, smoke density, oxygen content and carbon dioxide in the fireground building. External wind speed and direction, humidy and atmospheric pressure are also recorded. The fireground buildings are designed and constructed in such a way that realistic fires may be staged in them repeatedly without serious damage to the fabric. They include a drill tower of eight floors and a basement containing a smoke and heat generating room, lift gear and sewers; an industrial block of two floors, which includes a warehouse and a fish and chip shop; a second, larger, multi-storied industrial block complete with lift and wet and dry risers; a three bedroomed house, a fully equipped electric transformer house; and a breathing apparatus training block incorporating search rooms, crawling galleries, fire house etc and an instructional area. There is also a simulated ship, with two ship's holds of some 1,500 ton capacity, which is realistically equipped and stands in four feet of water alongside a quay and cargo shed. All these buildings have been designed and equipped so as to enable students to gain practical experience of all the problems which might arise at actual fires.

Other facilities on the fireground include a substantial oil tank, oil trays and 2,500 gallon oil tanker; two propane gas tanks; an electrical grid carrying voltages up to 30,000; an area for simulating leaking gas mains and anothersfor fires of metals and other hazardous materials. The College is equipped with a full range of fire-fighting equipment and a comprehensive fleet of 27 fire appliances.

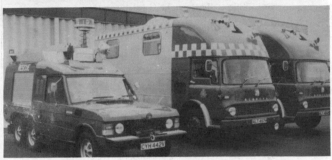

Picture on this & previous pages show: 1. WrLs & WrT/Ls (from left): OYH 414R, GUL 273W, GJD 805N, CYH 440V, VLU 206G, VLU 205G. 2. WrT/L, WrT & PEs (from left): KUC 701P, GJD 806N, GJD 807N, ULR 69F, ALT 468H. 3. HPs & TLPs (from left): KYY 295X. VLU 214G, ULR 68F, ULR 67F. 4. L4R (CYH 442V), CU (ALT 467H) & CIU/DU (ALT 466H). 5. Reynolds-Boughton/Chubb Pacesetter WrL (OHY 417R).

PRINCIPAL OFFICERS

Commandant: D. Blacktop Esq., CBE, FIFireE.
Deputy Commandant: D. Holland Esq., MBE, MIFireE.
Assistant Commandant: J.C. Maxwell Esq., OBE, DFC, QFSM.
Director of Studies: D.H. Walwyn-James Esq., MA.

APPLIANCE FLEET LIST

Type	Reg. No.	Make	Body
WrL	NYL 736Y	Bedford TKG (d)	Saxon
WrL	NYL 737Y	Bedford TKG (d)	Saxon
WrL	NYL 738Y	Bedford TKG (d)	Saxon
WrT/L	GUL 273W	Bedford TKG (d)	Carmichael
WrT/L	GUL 274W	Bedford TKG (d)	Carmichael
WrT/L	CYH 438V	Dennis RS/Perkins	Dennis
WrT/L	CYH 439V	Dennis RS/Perkins	Dennis
WrT/L	CYH 440V	Dennis RS/Perkins	Dennis
WrT/L	TYE 886S	Dodge K1113/Perkins	HCB-Angus
WrT/L	TYE 887S	Dodge K1113/Perkins	HCB-Angus
WrL	OYH 414R	Bedford TKG (d)	HCB-Angus (CSV)
WrL	OYH 417R	Reynolds-Boughton/ (d)	Chubb (Pacesetter)
WrT/L	KUC 701P	ERF 84P/Perkins	ERF Firefighter
WrT/L	GJD 805N	Dodge K850/Perkins	HCB-Angus
WrT	GJD 806N	Dennis D/Perkins	Dennis
WrT/L	GJD 807N	Ford D (d)	Carmichael
WrL	VLU 206G	Dennis F108/Perkins	Dennis
WrL	VLU 205G	Bedford TK (d)	Carmichael
PE	* ALT 468H	Bedford TK (d)	HCB-Angus
PE	* ALT 469H	Bedford TK (d)	HCB-Angus
RV	ULR 69F	AEC (d)	Merryweather (ex.PE)
TLP	NYL 712Y	Shelvoke & Drewry/ Perkins	Carmichael/ Magirus (30m)
TLP	ULR 67F	AEC (d)	Merryweather (30m)
TLP	* ULR 68F	AEC (d)	Merryweather (30m)
HP	KYY 295X	Shelvoke & Drewry/ Perkins	Angloco/Simon (22m)
HP	* VLU 214G	Dennis/Perkins	Dennis/Simon (22m)
CIU/DU	ALT 466H	Bedford TK (d)	Plaxton
CU	ALT 467H	Bedford TK (d)	Plaxton
HL/ST	ALT 471H	Bedford (d)	Plaxton
ET	ALT 470H	Dennis F/Perkins	Dennis
FoT	CYH 441V	Dodge G/Perkins	Carmichael
L4R	CYH 442R	Range Rover 6X4	Carmichael Commando
Amb	CYH 435V	Bedford CF	Wadham

*Now sold.

RAF FIRE SERVICE

The RAF Fire Service has a number of stations including Quedgeley (Gloucester) with Bedford TK/HCB-Angus WrT 28 AG 55 and Bedford CF L2V 64 AM 50 (seen above). Below is Baverstock (Dinton), Wiltshire with Bedford TKG/Carmichael WrT 31 AG 62 and Land Rover L4V. On the next page are applicances at RAF Upavon, (Pewsey), Wiltshire. From top to bottom: Bedford/Pyrene Mark 8 CrT 27 AG 84; Land Rover/HCB-Angus TACR1 30 AG 67 and Range Rover/HCB-Angus TACR2 31 AG 60; Thornycroft/Dennis Mark 9 CrT 28 AJ 24.